Contents

Introduction

A vast amount of information concerning genealogy and family history is now available on the internet. Surfing the net can be a very productive process for the researcher; it can, however, also be very frustrating. Despite the fact that there are thousands of genealogical web sites worth visiting, the means for finding particular relevant sites are very poor: search engines frequently list dozens of irrelevant sites, but not the ones you require. This book is intended to help you identify those sites which are most likely to be relevant to your research. The listing is selective; I have only included those sites which are of general interest to most genealogists. Consequently, I have excluded sites devoted solely to particular families. The innumerable sites which are, in theory, international in scope, but in practice are primarily of interest to American genealogists, are also excluded, as are those sites which are of general, rather than specifically genealogical interest, e.g. general search engines, commercial sites such as Amazon, etc. Many of the sites which I have listed, especially those in chapters 1, 7 and 8 can be used to find these excluded categories.

Beginners should also consult:
CHRISTIAN, PETER. *Finding genealogy on the Internet.* David Hawgood, 1999. This book offers many suggestions which will help you to improve your surfing techniques.

It should be noted that http: should be prefixed to all URLs listed in this directory.

This listing is as up to date as I have been able to make it. However, new web pages are being mounted all the time, and URLs frequently change. Consequently, it is anticipated that this directory will need frequent updating. If you are unable to find a site listed here, then you should check Cyndis List or one of the other gateways listed in chapter 1 below; the probability is that the site has moved to another address. Alternatively, search words from the title - or the URL - on a search engine such as **www.google.com.** If you know of sites which have not been included here, please let me know so that they can be included in the next edition of this directory.

My thanks go to Cynthia Hanson, who has typed this book, to Bob Boyd, who has seen it through the press, and to the officers of the Federation of Family History Societies who kindly agreed to its publication.

Stuart A. Raymond

1. Gateways, Search Engines, etc.

There are a variety of gateways and search engines for Scottish genealogists. Cyndis list is the major international gateway, with a lengthy listing of Scottish websites. Genuki provides both extensive introductory information and links to innumerable sites. Quite a number of other sites offer similar help. General search engines are not listed here: they may be found on Cyndis List.

- Cyndis List
  www.CyndisList.com
This is also available in book format: HOWELLS, CYNDI. *Cyndis List: a comprehensive list of 70,000 genealogy sites on the internet.* 2nd ed. 2 vols. Baltimore: Genealogical Publishing, 2001.

- Genuki: Scotland
  www.genuki.org.uk/big/sct

- Scotland: Genealogy
  www.genuki.org.uk/big.sct/Genealogy.html
Links and bibliography

- Scotland Gen Web
  www.scotlandgenweb.org/

- Scotland Research: UK Genealogy
  www.ukgenealogy.co.uk/scotland.htm

- Genealogylinks.net
  www.genealogylinks.net/uk/scotland/index.html
Gateway

- Gengateway.com: Scottish Gateway
  www.gengateway.com/index.cfm?GID=22

- Genlink.Scotland
  www.genlink.btinternet.co.uk/scotland.htm
Gateway

- Links to Go
  www.links2go.com/topic/Scottish_Genealogy
Gateway

- My Favourite Resources for Scotland: primary, secondary, and other resources for the family historian
  www.geocities.com/Heartland/Meadows/5209/resct.htm
Brief gateway

- Rampant Scotland Directory: Genealogy
  www.rampantscotland.com/
Gateway

- Search Beat: Scotland Web and Internet Guide
  regional.searchbeat.com/scotland.htm
Gateway to general Scottish sites

- Scottish and LDS Genealogical Reference Information
  www.ktb.net/~dwills/scotref/13300-scottishreference.htm
Brief introductory information with links to a few important web-sites

- Tracing your Scottish Ancestry
  www.geo.ed.ac.uk/home/scotland/genealogy.html
Brief gateway

- Viv Dunstan's Indexes
  www.vivdunstan.co.uk
Notes on various indexes under compilation or planned for publication

- Scottish Genes Information Centre
  www.sirius.com/~black/webrings/gene/index.htm
Web ring

2. General Introductions to Scottish Genealogy

Genuki (see chapter 1) is probably the most comprehensive introductory site currently available. There are, however, numerous other introductory sites for the Scottish genealogist; some of these are listed here - although many of the other sites listed elsewhere in this directory also have useful introductory information.

- Beginning Scots-Irish (Ulster Scots) research
  hometown.aol.com/jilliemae/ulster1.htm
  Continued in /ulster2.htm

- BIFHS-USA Guide to British Isles Research: Scotland
  www.rootsweb.com/~bifhsusa/ressco.html/membersvc.html

- Drew's Scottish Genealogy & Ancestor Search
  members.aol.com/drewhss/drew.htm/

- Family History
  www.scan.org.uk/familyhistory/index.htm
  From the Scottish Archives Network

- Genealogy in Scotland
  www.web-ecosse.com/genes.htm

- How do I trace my Scottish Roots?
  www.visitscotland.com/faqs/detail__faq.asp?ID=61

- Introduction to Scottish Family History
  www.genuki.org.uk/big/sct/intro.html
  On-line tutorial

- Researching your Family History: Getting Started
  www.tartans.com/genealogy/

- Rootsweb Guide to Tracing Your Family Tree: Irish, Scotch-Irish, Scottish
  www.rootsweb.com/rwguide/lesson21.htm

- Scotland Genealogy
  www.rootsweb.com/~genclass/205/gen205.htm
  Introductory tutorial

- Tracing Your Scottish Ancestry
  www.geo.ed.ac.uk/home/Scotland/genealogy.html
  Introduction

For the wider picture, it may be useful to check sites of general historical interest. Visit:

- Cameron's Gateway to Scottish History
  members.tripod.co.uk/%7ECunninghamC/Homepage12__97/index.htm

- Scotland: History
  www.genuki.org.uk/big/sct/History.html

- SCRAN
  www.scran.ac.uk/homepage/
  Scottish history and culture

- Timeline of Scottish History
  www.nls.uk/scotlandspages/timeline.html

- Skye's Scottish History Timeline
  hometown.aol.com/Skylander/timeline.html

3. Libraries, Record Offices and Books

Most of the information sought by genealogists is likely to be found in books and archival sources. The libraries and record offices which hold these resources provide an essential genealogical service, which is unlikely to be replaced by the internet. The value of the latter is in pointing you in the right direction, and helping you to identify the books and records you need to check. Many libraries and record offices now have web pages, some of which are listed here. Those which provide internet access to their catalogues are providing a particularly valuable service.

It is impossible in the compass of this book to provide a complete list of library and record office web sites likely to be of use to genealogists. Such a list would have to include most public and university libraries, and is outside the scope of this book. However, a number of sites provide listings. See:

- Library and Archive Sources in Scotland
  www.ifb.co.uk/~kinman/arcnlib.html

- Scotland: Archives and Libraries
  www.genuki.org.uk/big/sct/Archives.html

- Familia: the UK and Ireland's Guide to Genealogical Sources in Public Libraries
  www.earl.org.uk/familia/main.html
  Directory of libraries of interest to genealogists

- The Scottish Universities: their libraries and archives
  members.ozemail.com.au/~jim/jimjargg.htm
  Guide for the genealogist

- Hytelnet: Library Catalogs: United Kingdom
  www.lights.com/hytelnet/uk0/uk000.html

- BUBL UK: Libraries
  www.bubl.ac.uk/libraries.htm
  Lists UK national, public and university libraries

- OBI-OPACS in Britain and Ireland: a directory of library catalogues and services in Britain and Ireland
  www.niss.ac.uk/lis/obi/obi.html

- Copac
  www.copac.ac.uk
  Union catalogue of 20 UK and Irish university libraries, including several major Scottish institutions

- The UK Public Libraries Page
  dspace.dial.pipex.com/town/square/ac940/ukpublib.html
  Lists public libraries on the Web, including those with on-line catalogues

- Scottish Archives Network
  www.scan.org.uk
  Includes a directory of repositories, and much general information

- Scottish Record Offices and Archives on the Web
  www.oz.net/~markhow/scotsros.htm

- UK Archival Repositories on the Internet
  www.archivesinfo.net/uksites.html
  Directory, including some Scottish repositories

- County Record Offices in England, Scotland, Wales and Northern Ireland
  genealogy.8k.com/main3.html
  Postal addresses only; no links

- Historical Manuscripts Commission: Archon
  www.hmc.gov.uk/archon.htm
Directory of archive repositories

- National Register of Archives
  www.hmc.gov.uk/nra/nra2.htm

- Historical Manuscripts Commission Sources for Genealogy
  www.hmc.gov.uk/main.htm
Listed in the National Register of Archives

Major Institutions

For links to the web-sites of major national repositories, visit:
- Family Records Portal
  www.familyrecords.gov.uk

British Library

- British Library
  www.bl.uk

- British Library Public Catalogue
  blpc.bl.uk/

- British Library Manuscripts Catalogue
  molcat.bl.uk

National Archives of Scotland

- National Archives of Scotland
  www.nas.gov.uk

- Published Guides and Sources: N.A.S. Factsheet
  www.nas.gov.uk/miniframe/resources/publishedguides.pdf

National Library of Scotland

- National Library of Scotland
  www.nls.uk

Public Record Office

- Public Record Office
  www.pro.gov.uk
The major British archives repository. Gives access to an extensive catalogue, and much, much more!

- An Overview of the Public Record Office Website
  www.genuki.org.uk/indexes/PROContents.html
Genuki's index to the P.R.O. site

Family History Library

- Family History Library
  www.familysearch.org
Library of the Latter Day Saints. Extensive site with numerous pages

- Family History Centres in Scotland
  www.familysearch.org/Eng/Library/FHC/
  FHC__Results.asp?FHCCountry=Scotland
Of the Latter Day Saints

National Museum of Scotland

- National Museum of Scotland: Scottish Life Archive
  www.nms.ac.uk/archive/frames.htm
Local Libraries and Archives

Aberdeenshire

- Aberdeen City Archives
  www.aberdeencity.gov.uk/acc/archivists.htm

- Aberdeenshire Archives and Libraries
  www.urie.demon.co.uk/genuki/ABD/archives.html
Overview

- University of Aberdeen: Historic Collections
  www.abdn.ac.uk/diss/heritage/
Extensive archives from the University and the locality

Angus

- Angus Archives and Libraries
  www.dundee.ac.uk/archives/genuki/ANS/Archives/welcome.htm
Overview

- Angus Local Studies Centre
  www.angus.gov.uk/history/archives/Default.htm

- Dundee City Archive & Record Centre
  www.dundeecity.gov.uk/archives/

- Dundee City Library Local Studies Department
  www.dundeecity.gov.uk/centlib/loc__stud.htm

- University of Dundee Archives
  www.dundee.ac.uk/archives/
The archives include the Brechin Diocesan archives, and many records of public and commercial organisations, estates, *etc.*

Argyll

- Argyll & Bute Council
  www.earl.org.uk/familia/services/scotland/argyle__bute.html

Ayrshire

- Ayrshire Archives and Libraries
  home.clara.net/iainkerr/genuki/AYR/archive.htm
Overview

- Ayrshire Roots genealogy
  www.ayrshireroots.com/Genealogy/Records/Archives/Archives.htm
Details of archive repositories and libraries for Ayrshire

- The Scottish & Local History Library
  www.rootsweb.com/~sctayr/southayr.html
Resources at Ayr Library

- Ayrshire Archives
  www.south__ayrshire.gov.uk/Archives/

- East Ayrshire Library Service
  www.rootsweb.com/~sctayr/eastayr.html
List of resources

- Ardrossan Local History Unit
  www.rootsweb.com/=sctayr/northayr.html
List of resources

Berwickshire

- The Scottish Borders Archives & Local History Centre
  www.rootsweb.com/~sctsel/Archives/Archives.htm
Covers Berwickshire, Peeblesshire, Roxburghshire and Selkirkshire
See also **www.familia.org.uk/services/scotland/borders.html**

Bute
See Argyll

Caithness

- The North Highland Archive
  www.highland.gov.uk/cl/publicservices/archivedetails/northarchive.htm
Covers Caithness, Sutherland, Ross & Cromarty, Invernessshire, and Nairnshire

Clackmannanshire

- Clackmannanshire Archives
  www.clacksweb.org.uk/dyna/archives
Official pages

- Clackmannanshire Archives
  www.dgnscrn.demon.co.uk/genuki/CLK/libraryPD.html
List of private deposits in Clackmannanshire Libraries from Genuki

- Clackmannanshire Library Resources
  www.dgnscrn.demon.co.uk/genuki/CLK/library.html

Dumfriesshire

- Dumfries & Galloway Archives
  www.dumgal.gov.uk/services/depts/comres/library/archives.htm

Dunbartonshire

- Dunbartonshire Libraries
  www.rootsweb.com/~sctdnb/libraries.html
  List of libraries with Dunbartonshire records
  See also Lanarkshire

Fife

- Fife Council Archive Centre
  www.genuki.org.uk/big/sct/FIF/libraries/Archives.htm
  Lists main holdings, with separate pages for parochial board/parish council records, school records, burgh and town council records, and various places.

- Cupar Library
  www.genuki.org.uk/big/sct/FIF/libraries/Cupar__lib.htm

- Dunfermline Central Library
  www.genuki.org.uk/big/sct/FIF/libraries/Dunfermline__Lib.htm

- Kirkcaldy Central Library
  www.genuki.org.uk/big/sct/FIF/libraries/Kirkcaldy__lib.htm

- Methil Library
  www.genuki.org.uk/big/sct/FIF/libraries/Methil__lib.htm

- St. Andrews Library (includes the Hay Fleming Library)
  www.genuki.org.uk/big/sct/FIF/libraries/HayFleming.htm

- St. Andrews University Library: Manuscripts and Muniments
  www-library.st-and.ac.uk/manusintro.htm
  Holds records of burghs, estates, and kirk sessions, *etc.*

Invernessshire

- The Highland Council Archive
  www.highland.gov.uk/cl/publicservices/archivedetails/highlandarchive.htm

Kincardineshire
See Aberdeenshire

Kinrossshire
See Perthshire

Kirkcudbrightshire
See Dumfires

Lanarkshire

- Glasgow City Libraries and Archives Online
  www.mitchelllibrary.org/

- Glasgow University Archives & Business Records Centre
  www.archives.gla.ac.uk/

Invernessshire

- Clan Donald Centre: Armadale Library and Study Centre
  www.highlandconnection.org/cdltstudy.html
  Library for Skye, the Western Isles and the West Highlands, run by the Clan Donald Lands Trust

- Strathclyde University Archives
  www.strath.ac.uk/Departments/Archives/

Midlothian

- City of Edinburgh Archives
  www.edinburgh.gov.uk/CEC/Corporate__Services/ Corporate__Communications/archivist/Edinburgh__City__Archives.html

- Midlothian District Library: Local Studies Centre
  www.genuki.org.uk/big/sct/MLN/LocalStudies.html

- Edinburgh City Libraries: Edinburgh Room
  www.edinburgh.gov.uk/servlet/Qs?IDC=CEC/Recreation/Leisure/Data/ Edinburgh__Room/Edinburgh__Room.idc

- Midlothian Local Studies Library
  www.midlothian.gov.uk/Community/Library/LibButs/Library__Home.asp

- Manuscript Collections in Edinburgh University Library: a user's guide
  www.lib.ed.ac.uk/lib/about/pubs/lg51/index.shtml

Moray

- Moray's Heritage
  www.moray.org/heritage/index.html
  Webpage for Moray Local Heritage Centre

Nairnshire
See Invernessshire

Orkney

- The Orkney Library and Archives
  www.genuki.org.uk/big/sct/OKI/archives.html

Peebleshire
See Berwickshire

Perthshire

- Perth & Kinross Council Libraries & Archives On-line
  www.pkc.gov.uk/library

- Perth & Kinross Council Archive
  www.scan.org.uk/directory/Perth/perthframeset.html

Renfrewshire
See Lanarkshire

Ross & Cromarty
See Invernessshire

Roxburghshire
See Berwickshire

Selkirkshire
See Berwickshire

Shetland

- Shetland Islands Council Archivist
  www.shetland.gov.uk/atoz/ed3.htm
Very brief

Stirlingshire

- Falkirk History Research Centre
  www.falkirkmuseums.demon.co.uk/museums.hrc/htm

Sutherland
See Invernessshire

West Lothian

- West Lothian Local History Library
  www.wlonline.org.uk/site/living/library/local/

Wigtownshire
See Dumfries

Books

It cannot be emphasized too strongly that books are as important to genealogical research as archives, and far more important than the internet. Bibliographies listing relevant books are essential reference works: the Scottish genealogist is fortunate that a number are available on the internet.

- A selected bibliography for Scottish Research in the N.Y.G. & B. Library
  www.nygbs.org/info/articles/Scottish__Bibliography.html
Based on the holdings of New York Genealogical & Biographical Society, but of value to all researchers

- Sources for Research in Scottish Genealogy
  lcweb.loc.gov/rr/genealogy/bib__quid/scotland.html
Valuable bibliography from the Library of Congress

- Sources for Scottish and Scots-American Genealogy
  wilson.lib.umn.edu/reference/sco-gene.html
Bibliography

- Texts and Calendars since 1982: a survey
  www.hmc.gov.uk/socs/over.htm
Bibliography of record society publications, including publications of some Scottish organizations

Aberdeenshire

- Aberdeenshire Bibliography
  www.urie.demon.co.uk/genuki/ABD/bibliography.html

Ayrshire
- Ayrshire Bibliography
  www.ayrshirehistory.org.uk/Bibliography/books__intro.htm

Kinrosshire
- Kinross Bibliography
  www.tulbol.demon.co.uk/bibliography.htm

Orkney
- Bibliography of Orkney Family Genealogies
  www.genuki.org.uk/big/sct/OKI/Families/pubgen.html

- Books relating to the history of the Orkney Islands
  www.genuki.org.uk/big/sct/OKI/history.html
Bibliography

4. Family History Societies

Most Scottish family history societies have web-sites. These generally provide information on the society - names of officers, meetings, membership information, publications, services offered, lists of members interests, *etc.* A full list of societies is available at:

- Family History and Genealogy Societies: Scotland
  www.genuki.org.uk/Societies/Scotland.html

- UK Genealogy Local Societies
  www.ukgenealogy.co.uk/societies.htm
Family History Society gateway

Reference may also be made to the list of societies in:
- Cyndis List: Scotland
  www.cyndislist.com/scotland.htm
and also to the membership list of the Scottish Association of Family History Societies (see below).

National Societies
- Scottish Association of Family History Societies
  www.safhs.org.uk

- Scottish Genealogy Society
  www.scotsgenealogy.com

- Scottish Genealogy Society
  www.tartans.com/articles/sgs.htm
Comments by a visitor

- Society of Genealogists
  www.sog.org.uk

- Anglo-Scottish Family History Society
  www.mlfhs.demon.co.uk/AngloScots
Part of the Manchester & Lancashire Family History Society

- Guild of One-Name Studies
  www.one-name.org/
- Heraldry Society of Scotland
  www.heraldry-scotland.co.uk/Homepage.htm

Overseas Societies

- Scottish Group, Genealogical Society of Queensland
  www.home.st.net/au/~dunn/scots.htm
- Scottish Interest Group, Western Australian Genealogical Society
  cleo.murdoch.edu.au/~wags/sigscot

County and Local Societies

Aberdeenshire

- Aberdeen & North-East Scotland Family History Society
  www.anesfhs.f9.co.uk

Angus
See Perthshire

Argyll
See Lanarkshire

Ayrshire

- Alloway & Southern Ayrshire Family History Society
  www.maybole.org/history/resources/asafhs.htm
- East Ayrshire Family History Society
  www.eastayrshirefhs.org.uk
- Largs & North Ayrshire Family History Society
  lnafhs.freeyellow.com/index.html
- Troon @ Ayrshire Family History Society
  www.troonayrshirefhs.org.uk

Banff
See under Aberdeenshire

Berwickshire

- Borders Family History Society
  www.vivdunstan.clara.net/genuki/misc/bordersFHS.html

Bute

- Isle of Arran Heritage Museum (Family History Society)
  www.btinternet.com/~tom.k.macleod/page2.html

See also Lanarkshire

Caithness

- The Highland Family History Society
  www.genuki.org.uk/big/scot/Highland.FHS.home.html

Clackmannanshire

- Central Scotland Family History Society
  www.csfhs.org.uk

Dumfriesshire

- Dumfries and Galloway Family History Society
  www.dgfhs.org.uk

Dunbartonshire
See Lanarkshire

East Lothian
See Midlothian

Fife

- Fife Family History Society
  www.fifefhs.pwp.blueyonder.co.uk

See also Perthshire

Invernessshire
See Caithness

Kincardineshire
See Aberdeenshire

Kinrossshire
See Perthshire

Kirkcudbrightshire
See Dumfriesshire

Lanarkshire
- Glasgow & West of Scotland Family History Society
  www.gwsfhs.org.uk/index2.html

- Lanarkshire Family History Society
  www.lanarkshirefhs.org.uk/home.html

Midlothian
- The Lothians Family History Society
  www.lothiansfhs.org.uk

Moray
See Aberdeenshire

Nairnshire
See Caithness

Orkney
- Orkney Family History Society
  www.genuki.org.uk/big/sct/OKI/ofhs.html

Peeblesshire
See Berwickshire

Perthshire
- Central Scotland Family History Society
  www.csfhs.org.uk

- Tay Valley Family History Society
  www.tayvalleyfhs.org.uk

Renfrewshire
- Renfrewshire Family History Society
  www.geocities.com/renfrewshirefhs

See also Lanarkshire

Roxburghshire
See Berwickshire

Selkirkshire
See Berwickshire

Shetland
- Shetland Family History Society
  www.users.zetnet.co.uk/shetland-fhs

Stirlingshire
See Clackmannanshire

Sutherland
See Caithness

West Lothian
- West Lothian Family History Society
  www.wlfhs.org.uk
See also Midlothian

Wigtownshire
See Dumfriesshire

5. Discussion Groups: Mailing Lists and Newsgroups

Want to ask someone who knows? Then join one of the groups listed here. For general information on mailing lists, visit:

- FAQ: Mailing Lists: What are they for?
  helpdesk.rootsweb.com/help/mail1.html

When you join a mailing list, you can send and receive messages from every other member of the list. By way of contrast, you do not have to join the Usenet newsgroups, but do need newsreading software if you want to read them in the traditional way. Alternatively, you can read them online, and post to them - like message boards - at:

- Usenet Discussion Forums
  groups.google.com/
Index to Usenet newsgroups.

The major Usenet newsgroup for Scotland is:

- soc.genealogy.britain
  groups.google.com/groups?hl=en&group=soc.genealogy.britain
Gatewayed to GENBRIT Mailing List (see below)

See also:

- Soc.Genealogy.Surnames.Britain
  www.news2mail.com/soc/genealogy/surnames/britain.html

The authoritative guide to mailing lists is John Fuller's

- Genealogy Resources on the Internet: United Kingdom Mailing Lists
  www.rootsweb.com/~jfuller/gen__mail__country-unk.htm

- Genealogy Mailing Lists (Genuki)
  www.genuki.org.uk/indexes/MailingLists.html

- British Isles Gen Web Project: Mailing Lists
  www.britishislesgenweb.org/mailinglists.html

- Cyndis List
  www.CyndisList.com/mailing.htm

Many mailing lists are hosted by Rootsweb. These are listed at:

- Genealogy Mailing Lists at Rootsweb
  lists.rootsweb.com

All mailing lists hosted by Rootsweb are archived. To search these archives, visit:

- Roots-L Search Page
  searches.rootsweb.com/roots-l.html

- Genealogy of the Isles: Scotland E-mail Mailing Lists
  www.io.com/~crberry/isles/mailinglist__scotland.html
List of mailing lists

- Scotland Related Mailing Lists
  www.scotlandgenweb.org/scotlandmail.html

- UKGenealogy: list of mailing lists
  www.ukgenealogy.co.uk/lists.htm
List of those hosted by Rootsweb

GENERAL LISTS

- SCOTLAND Mailing List
  lists.rootsweb.com/index/intl/SCT/SCOTLAND.html

- Scotland Genweb Mailing List
  lists.rootsweb.com/index/intl/SCT/SCOTLAND-GENWEB.html

- SCOTLAND-ROLLCALL Mailing List
  lists.rootsweb.com/intl/SCT/SCOTLAND-ROLLCALL.html

- Scotland-Roots Mailing List
  lists.rootsweb.com/index/intl/SCT/SCOTLAND-ROOTS.html

- Scots International
  groups.yahoo.com/group/scotsinternational

- Southern Scotland Genealogy
  groups.yahoo.com/group/SouthernScotlandGenealogy
Discussion group

SPECIAL INTEREST LISTS

- CANADIAN ULSTER SCOTS Mailing List
  lists.rootsweb.com/index/intl/CAN/CANADIAN-ULSTER-SCOTS.html

- Celts Mailing List
  lists.rootsweb.com/index/intl/SCT/CELTS.html

- Ethnic-Scots: NCSCOTS Mailing List
  lists.rootsweb.com/index/other/Ethnic-Scots/NCSCOTS.html
Immigrants to North Carolina

- Ethnic-Scots: CAPE-FEAR-SCOTS Mailing List
  lists.rootsweb.com/index/other/Ethnic-Scots/CAPE-FEAR-SCOTS.html
Immigrants to Cape Fear region of North Carolina

- Scotland-Cemeteries Mailing List
  lists.rootsweb.com/index/intl/SCT/SCOTLAND-CEMETERIES.html

- Clans Mailing List
  lists.rootsweb.com/index/intl/SCL/CLANS.html

- The Highland Clearances email mailing list
  www.macgowan.org/emmaillis.html

- Jacobites Mailing List
  lists.rootsweb.com/index/intl/SCT/JACOBITES.html

- SCT-GEN-MEDIEVAL Mailing List
  lists.rootsweb.com/index/intl/SCT/SCT-GEN-MEDIEVAL.html

- SCT-ROYAL Mailing List
  lists.rootsweb.com/index/intl/SCT/SCT-ROYAL.html

- Scottish-Mining Mailing List
  lists.rootsweb.com/index/intl/SCT/SCOTTISH-MINING.html

- Scotland-Obits Mailing List
  lists.rootsweb.com/index/intl/SCT/SCOTLAND-OBITS.html

- Scottish War Prisoners
  groups.yahoo.com/group/scottishwarprisoners
For Covenanters imprisoned in England, mid-17th c.

- SCT-GEN-MEDIEVAL Mailing List
  lists.rootsweb.com/index/intl/SCT/SCT-GEN-MEDIEVAL.html

- SCT-TOMBSTONE-INSCRIPTIONS Mailing List
  lists.rootsweb.com/index/intl/SCT/SCT-TOMBSTONE-INSCRIPTIONS.html

- WGW-SURNAMES-SCOTLAND Mailing List
  lists.rootsweb.com/index/intl/SCT/WGW-SURNAME SCOTLAND.html

- Gen-Trivia-Scotland Mailing List
  lists.rootsweb.com/index/intl/SCT/GEN-TRIVIA-SCOTLAND.html

COUNTY AND LOCAL LISTS

Aberdeenshire

- Aberdeen Mailing List
  lists.rootsweb.com/index/intl/SCT/ABERDEEN.html

See also Nairnshire

Angus

- Angus Mailing List
  lists.rootsweb.com/index/intl/SCT/ANGUS.html

Argyll

- SCT-ARGYLL Mailing List
  lists.rootsweb.com/index/intl/SCT/SCT-ARGYLL.html

- SCT-ARL-TIREE Mailing List
  lists.rootsweb.com/index/intl/SCT/SCT-ARL-TIREE.html

- **SCT-WIS Mailing List**
  lists.rootsweb.com/index/intl/SCT/SCT-WIS.html
Covers the Western Isles, which were in the counties of Argyll, Invernessshire, and Ross & Cromarty
- Isle of Islay Mailing Group
  homepages.rootsweb.com/~steve/islay/maillist.htm
- **SCT-ISLAY Mailing List**
  lists.rootsweb.com/index/intl/SCT/SCT-ISLAY.html
- **SCT-ISLE OF MULL Mailing List**
  lists.rootsweb.com/index/intl/SCT/SCT-ISLE OF MULL.html

Ayrshire
- Ayrshire Mailing List
  lists.rootsweb.com/index/intl/SCT/AYRSHIRE.html

Banffshire
- SCT-BANFFSHIRE Mailing List
  lists.rootsweb.com/index/intl/SCT/SCT-BANFFSHIRE.html

See also Moray and Nairnshire

Berwickshire
- SCT-BERWICK Mailing List
  lists.rootsweb.com/index/intl/SCT/SCT-BERWICK.html

Buteshire
- Buteshire Genweb Mailing List
  lists.rootsweb.com/index/intl/SCT/ButeshireGenWeb.html

Caithness
- SCT-CAITHNESS Mailing List
  lists.rootsweb.com/index/intl/SCT/SCT-CAITHNESS.HTML

Clackmannanshire
- SCT-CLACKMANNANSHIRE Mailing List
  lists.rootsweb.com/index/intl/SCT/SCT-CLACKMANNANSHIRE.html

Dumfriesshire
- Dumfries-Galloway Mailing List
  lists.rootsweb.com/index/intl/SCT/DUMFRIES-GALLOWAY.html

Dunbartonshire
- Dunbartonshire-Genweb Mailing List
  lists.rootsweb.com/index/intl/SCT/DUNBARTONSHIRE-GENWEB.html

East Lothian
- Mailing Lists [East Lothian]
  hometown.aol.com/eastlothiangen/index.html
- SCT-EAST-LOTHIAN Mailing List
  lists.rootsweb.com/index/intl/SCT/SCT-EAST-LOTHIAN.html

Fife
- SCT-FIFE Mailing List
  lists.rootsweb.com/index/intl/SCT/SCT-FIFE.html

Invernessshire
- SCT-INVERNESS Mailing List
  lists.rootsweb.com/index/intl/SCT/SCT-INVERNESS.html

See also Argyll and Nairnshire

Kincardineshire
- SCT-KINCARDINE Mailing List
  lists.rootsweb.com/index/intl/SCT/SCT-KINCARDINE.html
- Stonehaven Genealogy
  groups.yahoo.com/group/Stonehaven__Genealogy

See also Nairnshire

Kinrossshire
- SCT-KINROSS Mailing List
  lists.rootsweb.com/index/intl/SCT/SCT-KINROSS.html

Kirkcudbrightshire

- SCT-KIRKCUDBRIGHTSHIRE Mailing List
  lists.rootsweb.com/index/intl/SCT/SCT-KIRKCUDBRIGHTSHIRE.html

See also Dumfriesshire

Lanarkshire

- Lanark Mailing List
  lists.rootsweb.com/index/intl/SCT/LANARK.html

- SCT-LKS-SHOTTS Mailing List
  lists.rootsweb.com/index/intl/SCT/SCT-LKS-SHOTTS.html
Covers Shotts, Lanarkshire

- SCT-GLASGOW Mailing List
  lists.rootsweb.com/index/intl/SCT/SCT-GLASGOW.html

Midlothian

- Midlothian Mailing List
  lists.rootsweb.com/index/intl/SCT/MIDLOTHIAN.html

- SCT-EDINBURGH Mailing List
  lists.rootsweb.com/index/intl/SCT/SCT-EDINBURGH.html

Moray

- Moray Mailing List
  lists.rootsweb.com/index/intl/SCT/MORAY.html
Covers Banffshire and Nairnshire, as well as Moray

See also Nairnshire

Nairnshire

- SCT-NAIRNSHIRE Mailing List
  lists.rootsweb.com/index/intl/SCT/SCT-NAIRNSHIRE.html

- SCT-NECOAST Mailing List
  lists.rootsweb.com/index/intl/SCT/SCT-NECOAST.html
Covers the coast of Nairnshire, Moray, Banffshire, Aberdeenshire and
Kincardineshire

- SCT-STRATHNAIRN Mailing List
  lists.rootsweb.com/index/intl/SCT/SCT-STRATHNAIRN.html
Covers Nairnshire and N.E.Invernessshire

See also Moray

Orkney

- Orcadia Mailing List
  lists.rootsweb.com/index/intl/SCT/ORCADIA.html

- Orkney Mailing List
  lists.rootsweb.com/index/intl/SCT/ORKNEY.html

Peeblesshire

- SCT-PEEBLES-SHIRE Mailing List
  lists.rootsweb.com/index/intl/SCT/SCT-PEEBLES-SHIRE.html

Perthshire

- Perthshire Mailing List
  lists.rootsweb.com/index/intl/SCT/PERTHSHIRE.html

Renfrewshire

- SCT-RENFREW Mailing List
  lists.rootsweb.com/index/intl/SCT/SCT-RENFREW.html

Ross & Cromarty

- Rossgen Mailing List
  lists.rootsweb.com/index/intl/SCT/ROSSGEN.html
See also Argyll

Roxburghshire

- SCT-ROXBURGH Mailing List
  lists.rootsweb.com/index/intl/SCT/SCT-ROXBURGH.html

Selkirkshire

- SCT-SELKIRK Mailing List
  lists.rootsweb.com/index/intl/SCT/SCT-SELKIRK.html

Shetland
- SCT-SHETLAND Mailing List
  lists.rootsweb.com/index/intl/SCT/SCT-SHETLAND.html

Stirlingshire
- SCT-STIRLINGSHIRE
  lists.rootsweb.com/index/intl/SCT/SCT-STIRLINGSHIRE.html

Sutherland
- SCT-SUTHERLAND Mailing List
  lists.rootsweb.com/index/intl/SCT/SCT-SUTHERLAND.html

- SCT-SUT-TONGUE Mailing List
  lists.rootsweb.com/index/intl/SCT/SCT-SUT-TONGUE.html

Wigtownshire
- SCT-WIGTOWNSHIRE Mailing List
  lists.rootsweb.com/index/intl/SCT/SCT-WIGTOWNSHIRE.html
See also Dumfriesshire

6. Message/Query Boards

A number of websites offer you the opportunity to post messages/queries on the site itself. Some of these sites will also email the messages to subscribers. Message boards for every Scottish county can be found at:

- Rootsweb Message Boards: Scotland
  boards.ancestry.com/
  mbexec?htx=board&r=rw&p=localities.britisles.scotland

And also at:
- Message Boards / Forum for Scotland
  www.iprom.co.uk/forum/default2.asp?Name=Scotland&FID=4

Other general query boards include:
- Genealogy of the Isles: Scotland Query Board
  www.io.com/~crberry/isles/Queries/scotland_query01.html

- Scotland Gen Web Unknown County Query and Surname Board
  www.britishislesgenweb.org/cgi-bin/data/scotland.cgi

- Scottish Archive Network Forum
  www.scan.org.uk/forum/upload/index.php

Separate message boards for History and Archives, Genealogy and Scan

- WorldWide Genealogy Forum: Scotland
  forum.compuserve.com/gvforums/UK/default.asp?SRV=WWGenealogy

- The Gathering of the Clans: Tartans Bulletin Board
  www.tartans.com/cgi-bin/ubbcgi/Ultimate.cgi?action=intro

For a special interest forum, see:
- Scottish Military Historical Society Discussion Forum
  groups.yahoo.com/group/scottish_military

Aberdeenshire
- Aberdeenshire Message Boards
  www.scotlandgenweb.org/~aberdeen/queries.htm

Angus

- Angus Scotland Gen Web Query and Surname Board
  www.britishislesgenweb.org/cgi-bindata/angus.cgi

Ayrshire

- East Ayrshire Family History
  pub9.ezboard.com/beastayrshirefamilyhistory
  Bulletin Board

- Message Centre
  www.maybole.org/history/messagecentre.htm
  Message Board for research in Maybole

Banffshire

- Banffshire Scotland Genweb Query and Surname Board
  www.britishislesgenweb.org/cgi-bin/data/banffshire.cgi

Berwickshire

- Berwickshire Scotland Genweb Query and Surname Board
  www.britishislesgenweb.org/cgi-bin/data/berwickshire.cgi

Bute

- Bute Chat & Discussion Forums
  www.isle-of-bute.com/forumintro.htm

Caithness

- Caithness Gen Web Message Board
  zone1.accessboards.com/messageboard/evelyn.htm

Clackmannanshire

- Clackmannanshire Scotland Gen Web Query and Surname Board
  www.britishislesgenweb.org/cgi-bin/data/clackmannanshire.cgi

East Lothian

- East Lothian, Scotland Gen Web Query and Surname Board
  hometown.aol.com/eastlothiangen/index.html

- Lothians Family History Society Noticeboard
  www.lothiansfhs.org.uk/noticeboard.htm
  Message board for East Lothian, Midlothian, and West Lothian

Kinrossshire

- Kinross-shire Scotland Gen Web Query and Surname Board
  www.britishislesgenweb.org/cgi-bin/data/kinross.cgi

- The Kinross-shire Forum
  www.tulbol.demon.co.uk/forum.htm>

Lanarkshire

- Lanarkshire, Scotland Gen Web Query and Surname Board
  www.britishislesgenweb.org/cgi-bin/data/lanarkshire.cgi

- Noticeboard
  www.lanarkshirefhs.org.uk/home.html
  Message board hosted by Lanarkshire Family History Society

Midlothian
See East Lothian

Moray

- Moray Scotland Gen Web Query and Surname Board
  www.britishislesgenweb.org/cgi-bin/data/moray.cgi

Nairnshire

- Nairnshire, Scotand Gen Web Query and Surname Board
  www.britishislesgenweb.org/cgi-bin/data/nairnshire.cgi

Orkney

- The Orknet Genealogy Board
  www.orknet.co.uk/genboard/wwwboard.htm
  Bulletin Board

Peeblesshire

- Peeblesshire Scotland Gen Web Query Board
  www.britishislesgenweb.org/cgi-bin/data/peebleshire.cgi

Perthshire

- Perthshire, Scotland Gen Web Query and Surname Board
  www.britishislesgenweb.org/cgi-bin/data/perthshire.cgi

Renfrewshire

- Renfrewshire Scotland Gen Web Query and Surname Board
  www.britishislesgenweb.org/cgi-bin/data/renfrewshire.cgi

7. County Pages

A great deal of information is to be found on genealogical county and local pages. A few individuals have created their own pages, but three organizations have provided pages for every Scottish county. Genuki provides the most useful pages, concentrating attention on primary historical information, rather than ongoing and completed research; it has many pages on particular parishes (which are not separately listed here). Genweb has some similar information, but also includes query boards for each county (listed in chapter 6), and has more information on current and completed family history research. UKGenealogy offers a wide range of general information on resources.

Aberdeenshire

- Aberdeenshire Genuki
  www.urie.demon.co.uk/genuki/ABD/

- Aberdeenshire Genweb
  www.rootsweb.com~sctabd/

- Aberdeenshire-Scotland (ABD) UK Genealogy
  www.ukgenealogy.co.uk/abd.htm

- Peterhead Genealogy
  axs.com.au/~wsb
Includes various source indexes, *etc.*

Angus

- Angus Genuki
  www.dundee.ac.uk/archives/genuki/ANS/

- Angus (Forfar) Genweb
  www.scotlandgenweb.org/~angus/

- ANGUS UK Genealogy
  www.ukgenealogy.co.uk/ans.htm

Argyll

- Argyll Genuki
  www.roe.ac.uk/genuki/arl/

- Argyllshire Genweb
  www.scotlandroyalty.org/argyll/argyllshire.html

- Argyllshire (ARL) UK Genealogy
  www.ukgenealogy.co.uk?arl/html

- Colonsay Family History
  www.colonsay.org.uk/geneal.html

- Isle of Mull Family History
  web.ukonline.co.uk/ian.phillips/mull/index.htm

- Skipness Parish, Argyllshire, Scotland, Records
  people.ne.mediaone.net/priestner/Skipness/Skipness.htm

A variety of original sources, some of them listed elsewhere in this directory

- Western Isles Genweb
  www.rootsweb.com/~sctwis/index.html

Covers parts of Argyll, Invernessshire, and Ross & Cromarty

Ayrshire

- Ayrshire Genuki
  home.clara.net/iainkerr/genuki/AYR/

- Ayrshire Genweb
  www.rootsweb.com/~sctayr/index.html

- Ayrshire UK Genealogy
  www.ukgenealogy.co.uk/ayr/htm

- The Ayrshire Page
  homepages.rootsweb.com/~ayrshire/

- Ayrshire Roots
  www.ayrshireroots.com

Extensive county pages, many listed elsewhere in this directory

Banffshire

- Banffshire Genuki
  www.genuki.org.uk/big/sct/BAN/index.html

- Banffshire Genweb
  www.scotlandgenweb.org/~banff/

- Banffshire UK Genealogy
  www.ukgenealogy.co.uk/ban.htm

Berwickshire

- Berwickshire Genuki
  www.genuki.org.uk/big/sct/BEW/

- Berwickshire Genweb
  www.rootsweb.com/~sctbew/

- Berwickshire UK Genealogy
  www.ukgenealogy.co.uk/bew.htm

Buteshire

- Buteshire (islands of Arran and Bute) Genuki
  www.skylinc.net/~lasmith/genuki/BUT/

- Buteshire Genweb
  www.rootsweb.com/~sctbutes/

- Buteshire UK Genealogy
  www.ukgenealogy.co.uk/but.htm

- Buteshire Family History Project
  www.geocities.com/buteshire

Transcripts of various original sources

Caithness

- Caithness Genuki
  www.frayston.demon.co.uk/genuki/cai/

- Caithness Genweb
  www.elbon24.freeserve.co.uk/Caithness.htm
- Caithness UK Genealogy
  www.ukgenealogy.co.uk/cai.htm

Clackmannanshire
- Clackmannanshire Genuki
  www.dgnscrn.demon.co.uk/genuki/CLK/
- Clackmannanshire Genweb
  www.scotlandgenweb.org/~clackmannan/
- Clackmannanshire UK Genealogy
  www.ukgenealogy.co.uk/clk.htm

Dumfriesshire
- Dumfriesshire Genuki
  www.embra.force9.co.uk/genuki/DFS/
- Dumfriesshire Genweb
  www.rootsweb.com/~sctdfs/
- Dumfries-shire UK Genealogy
  www.ukgenealogy.co.uk.dfs.htm
- The Scottish Page, dedicated to the research of Scottish Ancestry, especially that of Dumfries-Galloway
  homepages.rootsweb.com/~scottish

Dunbartonshire
- Dunbartonshire Genuki
  www.skyline.net/~lasmith/genuki/DNB/
- Dunbartonshire Genweb
  www.rootsweb.com/~sctdnb/index.htm
- Dunbartonshire UK Genealogy
  www.ukgenealogy.co.uk/dnb.htm

East Lothian
- East Lothian Genuki
  freespace.virgin.net/david/howie/genuki/ELN/index.html
- East Lothian Genweb
  hometown.aol.com/eastlothiangen/index.html
- East Lothian UK Genealogy
  www.ukgenealogy.co.uk/eln.htm

Fife
- Fife Genuki
  www.genuki.org.uk/big/sct/FIF/
- Fife Genweb
  www.rootsweb.com/~sctfif/
- Fife UK Genealogy
  www.ukgenealogy.co.uk/fif.htm
- The Fife Post
  www.fifepost.freeserve.co.uk/
Includes a county genealogy page

Forfarshire
See Angus

Invernessshire
- Inverness-shire Genuki
(includes Lewis (part), Uist and Skye)
  www.roe.ac.uk/genuki/inv/index.html
- Inverness-shire Genweb
  www.jansdigs.com/Inverness/index.html
- Inverness-shire UK Genealogy
  www.ukgenealogy.co.uk/inv.htm
- Family Tree Research in the Outer Hebrides of Scotland
  www.hebrides.com/coleis
Commercial page with useful general information
See also Argyll

Kincardineshire

- Kincardineshire Genuki
  www.genuki.org.uk/big/sct/KCD/index.html

- Kincardineshire Genweb
  www.rootsweb.com/~sctkcd/

- Kincardineshire UK Genealogy
  www.ukgenealogy.co.uk/kcd.htm

- Stonehaven Roots
  www.geocities.com/thistleinn

Kinrossshire

- Kinross-shire Genuki
  www.dgnscrn.demon.co.uk/genuki/KRS/

- Kinross-Shire Genweb
  www.rootsweb.com/~sctkrs/

- Kinross-shire UK Genealogy
  www.ukgenealogy.co.uk/krs.htm

- Exploring Kinross's history
  www.tulbol.demon.co.uk/history.htm

Kirkcudbrightshire

- Kirkcudbrightshire Genuki
  www.burgoyne.com/pages/djaggi/genuki/kirkcudb.htm

- Kirkcudbrightshire Genweb
  www.geocities.com/Heartland/Plains/8379/kirk.html

- Kirkcudbrightshire UK Genealogy
  www.ukgenealogy.co.uk/kkd/htm

Lanarkshire

- Lanarkshire Genuki
  www.genuki.org.uk/big/sct/LKS/index.htm

- Lanarkshire Genweb
  www.rootsweb.com/~sctlks/

- Lanarkshire UK Genealogy
  www.ukgenealogy.co.uk/lks.htm

- Lanark(shire) Miscellany
  www.scottap.com/family/Lanark/

Midlothian

- Midlothian Genuki
  www.btinternet.com/~mmgene/genuki/mln/

- Midlothian Genweb
  www.rootsweb.com/~sctmln/

- Midlothian UK Genealogy
  www.ukgenealogy.co.uk/mln.htm

Moray

- Moray Genuki
  www.genuki.org.uk/big/sct/MOR/index.html

- Moray Genweb
  www.scotlandgenweb.org/~moray/

- Morayshire UK Genealogy
  www.ukgenealogy.co.uk/mor.htm

Nairnshire

- Nairnshire Genuki
  www.genuki.org.uk/big/sct/NAI/index.html

- Nairnshire Genweb
  www.scotlandgenweb.org/~nairn/

- Nairnshire UK Genealogy
  www.ukgenealogy.co.uk/nai.htm

Orkney

- Orkney Genuki
  www.genuki.org.uk/big/sct/OKI/index.html

- Orkney Genweb
  www.scotlandgenweb.org/~orkney/

- Orkney UK Genealogy
  www.ukgenealogy.co.uk/oki.htm

Peeblesshire

- Peeblesshire Genuki
  www.genuki/org.uk/big/sct/PEE/

- Peeblesshire Genweb
  www.rootsweb.com/~sctpbs/

- Peebles-shire UK Genealogy
  www.ukgenealogy.co.uk/pee.htm

Perthshire

- Perthshire Genuki
  www.taybank.freeserve.co.uk/genuki/PER/

- Perthshire Genweb
  www.rootsweb.com/~sctper/

- Perthshire UK Genealogy
  www.ukgenealogy.co.uk/per.htm

- Genealogy
  www.rannoch.net/Genealogy.htm
Rannoch area, Perthshire

Renfrewshire

- Renfrewshire Genuki
  www.skyline.net/~lasmith/genuki/RFW/

- Renfrewshire Genweb
  www.scotlandgenweb.org/~renfrew/

- Renfrewshire UK Genealogy
  www.ukgenealogy.co.uk/rfw.htm

Ross & Cromarty

- Ross & Cromarty (includes parts of Lewis)
  www.roe.ac.uk/genuki/roc/index.html

- Ross & Cromarty Genweb
  www.rootsweb.com/~sctroc/

- Ross & Cromarty UK Genealogy
  www.ukgenealogy.co.uk/roc.htm

- Some Coigach Genealogy
  freepages.genealogy.rootsweb.com/~coigach/

See also Argyll

Roxburghshire

- Roxburghshire Genuki
  www.genuki.org.uk/big/sct/ROX/

- Roxburghshire Genweb
  www.elbon24.freeserve.co.uk/roxburgh.htm

- Roxburghshire UK Genealogy
  www.ukgenealogy.co.uk/rox.htm

Selkirkshire

- Selkirkshire Genuki
  www.genuki.org.uk/big/sct/SEL/

- Selkirkshire Genweb
  www.rootsweb.com/~sctsel/

- Selkirkshire UK Genealogy
  www.ukgenealogy.co.uk/sel.htm

Shetland

- Shetland Genuki
  www.genuki.org.uk/big/sct/SHI/index.html

- Shetland Islands Genweb
  www.rootsweb.com/~sctshi/

- Shetland UK Genealogy
  www.ukgenealogy.co.uk/shi.htm

Stirlingshire
- Stirlingshire Genuki
  www.genuki.org.uk/big/sct/STI/index.html
- Stirlingshire Genweb
  www.rootsweb.com/~sctsti/
- Stirlingshire UK Genealogy
  www.ukgenealogy.co.uk/sti.htm

Sutherland
- Sutherland Genuki
  www.genuki.org.uk/big/sct/SUT/index.html
- Sutherland Genweb
  members.aol.com/obrienbarb/Scot/SuthGenWeb.htm
- Sutherland UK Genealogy
  www.ukgenealogy.co.uk/sut.htm

West Lothian
- West Lothian (Linlithgowshire) Genuki
  www.btinternet.com/~mmgene/genuki/wln/index.htm
- West Lothian Genweb
  www.rootsweb.com/~sctwln2/
- West Lothian UK Genealogy
  www.ukgenealogy.co.uk/wln.htm

Wigtownshire
- Wigtownshire Genuki
  www.burgoyne.com/pages/djaggi/genuki.county1/wigtown.htm
- Wigtownshire Genweb
  www.rootsweb.com/~sctwig/wigtown.html
- Wigtownshire UK Genealogy
  www.ukgenealogy.co.uk/wig.htm

8. Surnames

The Internet is an invaluable aid for those who want to make contact with others researching the same surname. There are innumerable personal and family web-pages, surname mailing lists, and lists of surname interests. The first two categories are far too numerous to list here; this chapter will primarily be devoted to websites listing surname interests. However, for a general discussion of surnames on the web, see:

- Finding Surname Interests
  www.hawgood.co.uk/finding.htm

There are a number of international sites likely to assist in identifying surname sites - although they all have an American bias:

- Cyndis List: Databases, Search Sites, Surname Lists
  www.cyndislist.com/database.htm
- Cyndis List: Personal Home Pages
  www.cyndislist.com/personal.htm
Good starting point
- Cyndis List: Surnames, Family Association, & Family Newsletters Index
  www.cyndislist.com/surnames.htm
- Web Sites at Rootsweb
  www.rootsweb.come/~websites/
Select "Surname web sites'. Probably the most extensive listing of surname sites

A wide variety of websites, and all Rootsweb message boards, can be searched at:
- Surname Helper Home Page
  surhelp.rootsweb.com

- Surname Resources at Rootsweb
  resources.rootsweb.com/~clusters/surnames/index.html
Not just family web pages, but a wide range of other resources too

For more local listings, see:
- Scottish Clan and Family Associations
  clan-maccalum-malcolm.3acres.org/ScotClanFamily.html
Web directory

- Celtic Net Directory of Scottish Clans
  www.majestictech.com/the-celtic-net/clandirectory.html
Gateway to clan sites

Buteshire
- Buteshire Family History Project: One Name Studies
  www.geocities.com/buteshire/One%20Name%20Studies/
  one__name__studies.htm
Includes a number of family web-pages

- List of Bute Researchers Home Pages
  www.rootsweb.com/~sctbutes/homepage.htm

Orkney
- Orkney Genealogies on the Web
  www.genuki.org.uk/big/sct/OKI/Families/webgen.html
List of family homepages

Interest Lists
Many sites provide names and addresses of researchers seeking information on particular surnames. The most substantial of these sites is:

- Rootsweb Surname List
  rsl.rootsweb.com/cgi-bin/rslsql.cgi
International in scope: probably the biggest interests list on the web

Other major sites include:
- Surname Lists
  www.genuki.org.uk/indexes/SurnamesLists.html

- National Genealogical Survey: UK Surname Research Directory
  www.familyhistory.uk.com/
Interests list

- On-line Scottish Names Research Directory
  www.users.on.net/proformat/sctnames.html

- Scotland Surnames Listings
  www.county-surnames.co.uk/list.mv?county=Scotland

- **Scots on the Net**
  www.tartans.com/surnames
Interests list

If you want the most substantial interest list published in book format, visit:
- Genealogical Research Directory
  www.ozemail.com.au/~grdxxx
Webpage for ordering the book or CD

Aberdeenshire
- Aberdeenshire Surname List
  www.users.on.net/proformat/abdnames1.html

- Online Scottish Names Research Directory: Aberdeenshire
  www.users.on.net/proformat/abdnames1.html
Continued by **/abdnames2.html** and **abdnames3.html**

Angus
- Angus Surnames List
  www.geocities.com/Athens/Parthenon/5020/Angus/

Argyll
- Argyllshire, Scotland Surname List
  members.aol.com/sloinne/Argyll/Surnames.htm

- Isle of Mull Family History Pages: Surname Index
  www.ukonline.co.uk/ian.phillips/mull/index
Interest list with some details of what is already known, with separate page for 'birth or christening date index'

- People who are researching specific surnames in regards to the Isle of Islay
  homepages.rootsweb.com/~steve/islay/surnames.htm

Ayrshire

- Ayrshire Surnames Index Database
  home.clara.net/iainkerr/genuki/AYR/SID/indexsid.htm

- Maybole Surname Interests
  www.maybole.org/history/Surnames/surnamesac.htm

Banffshire

- Banffshire Surname List
  www.rootsweb.com/~sctban/

Berwickshire

- Berwickshire Surnames List
  www.vivdunstan.clara.net/genuki/BEW/Surnames/

Bute

- Bute Surname List
  www.users.on.net/proformat/butnames1.html

Caithness

- Genuki: Caithness County - Surnames List
  www.frayston.demon.co.uk/genuki/cai/surnames.htm

Clackmannanshire

- Genuki Clackmannanshire Surname List
  www.dgnscrn.demon.co.uk/genuki/CLK/misc/surnames/

Dumfriesshire

- Dumfries Surnames List
  www.users.on.net.proformat/dfsnames1.html

Dunbartonshire

- Dunbartonshire Surnames List
  www.rootsweb.com/~sctdnb/surnames.html

- Dunbartonshire Surname List
  www.users.on.net/proformat/dnbnames1.html

East Lothian

- East Lothian Surnames List
  www.vivdunstan.clara.net/genuki/ELN/Surnames/

Fife

- Kingdom of Fife Surnames List
  www.genuki.org.uk/big/scot/Fife/fife.surnames.html

Invernessshire

- Inverness Surnames List
  www.users.on.net/proformat/invnames1.html

Kincardineshire

- Kincardineshire Surname List
  www.users.on.net/proformat/kcdnames1.html

Kinrossshire

- Genuki Kinross-shire Surname List
  www.dgnscrn.demon.co.uk/genuki/KRS/misc/surnames/index.html

Kirkcudbrightshire

- Kirkcudbrightshire Surname List
  www.users.on.net/proformat/kkdnames1.html

Lanarkshire

- Lanarkshire Surname List
  freepages.genealogy.rootsweb.com/~slund/lanark.htm

- Members Interests Directory
  www.gwsfhs.org.uk/index2.html
Of the Glasgow & West of Scotland Family History Society

Midlothian

- Midlothian Surname List
  www.users.on.net/proformat/mlnnames1.html

Moray

- Morayshire Surname List
  www.users.on.net/proformat/mornames1.html

Nairnshire

- Nairn Surname List
  www.users.on.net/proformat/nainames1.html

Orkney

- Orkney Surname List
  www.users.on.net/proformat/okinames1.html

Peeblesshire

- Peeblesshire Surnames List
  www.vivdunstan.clara.net/genuki/PEE/Surnames/

Perthshire

- Perthshire Surname List
  www.users.on.net/proformat/pernames1.html

- Surnames in Highland Perthshire
  www.rannoch.net/Surnames/Index.htm
Interests list

- TVFHS Members Online & Mailing List
  www.tayvalleyfhs.org.uk/memweb.htm
Continued on /memweb2.htm
Interests page for Tay Valley Family History Society

Renfrewshire

- Renfrewshire Genealogical Surnames List
  members.madasafish.com/~andream/

Ross & Cromarty

- Ross & Cromarty Surname List
  www.users.on.net/proformat/rocnames1.html

Roxburghshire

- Roxburghshire Surname List
  www.vivdunstan.clara.net/genuki/ROX/Surnames/

Selkirkshire

- Selkirkshire Surnames List
  www.vivdunstan.clara.net/genuki/SEL/Surnames/

Shetland

- Shetland Surnames List
  www.users.on.net/proformat/shinames1.html

Stirlingshire

- County of Stirlingshire Surname List
  www.jeack.com.au/~treaclbk/surnames/stirling.htm

Sutherland

- County Sutherland, Scotland Surname List
  members.aol.com/sloinne/Sutherland/Surnames.htm

West Lothian

- West Lothian Surname List
  www.rootsweb.com/~sctwln

Wigtownshire

- Wigtownshire Surname List
  www.users.on.net/proformat/wignames1.html

9. Sources

Information on a wide range of sources is available on the net. This includes much valuable advice and a variety of source lists; it also includes a number of sites providing the actual data - although the latter are rarely of substantial size. For a useful general introduction to sources, consult:

- Interpreting Scottish Records
  www.ayrshireroots.com/Genealogy/Records/Legal%20Records.htm

Births, Marriages and Deaths
One of the most important sites for Scottish genealogists, including a number of valuable databases, is:

- Scots Origins: General Register Office for Scotland
  www.origins.net/GRO/
This includes: Old parish registers 1553 to 1854; statutory registers of births and marriages 1855 to 1899, statutory registers of deaths 1855 to 1924; census records for 1881; census records & images for 1891. This site charges fees for searches.

Other useful sites include:

- Birth, Marriage and Death Records in Scotland
  www.ktb.net/~dwills/scotref/13302-bmdtables.htm
List of films

- General Register Office for Scotland
  www.gro.scotland.gov.uk

- GROS birth/death/marriage certificates
  www.gro-scotland.gov.uk/grosweb.nsf/pages/bdm

- GROS family records
  www.gro-scotland.gov.uk/grosweb/grosweb.nst/pages/famrec/
Notes on G.R.O. records

30

- GROS: Old Parish Registers
  www.gro-scotland.gov.uk/grosweb/grosweb.nst/pages/opr
Notes with summary list

- List of the old parochial records
  www.gro-scotland.gov.uk/grosweb/grosweb.nst/pages/opr__cov

- Scotland BDM Exchange
  www.sctbdm.com/

- Scotland Genealogy: Parish Registers - Church Records of Scotland (Presbyterian); Non-conformist church records, kirk session records
  www.rootsweb.com/~genclass/205/gen205__5.htm

- Scotland Genealogy: civil registration and vital records
  www.rootsweb.com/~genclass/205/gen205__3.htm
Introductory tutorial

- Scotland & Ireland: Birth, Marriage & Death Records
  www.pro.gov.uk/research/easysearch/
  certificate%5Fenquiriesscotland.htm
Brief note

- Scotland: Parish Register Copies in the Library of the Society of Genealogists
  www.sog.org.uk/prc/sct.html

Angus

- Civil Registration: County of Angus
  www.personal.dundee.ac.uk/~amicoll/hist__stuff/civreg.htm

- Parish of Barry, Angus, Scotland, OPR: Burials 1746 to 1812
  freepages.genealogy.rootsweb.com/~shellypages/burldx.htm

- Extract from the old parish register for the Dundee (St. Peter parish), Scotland: burials 1837-1856
  www.monikiescotland.freeserve.co.uk/ah-saintpeter.htm

WWW. MONIKEE. ORG. UK

- Dunnichen Parish, Angus, Scotland: Interments 1856-76
  www.monikiescotland.freeserve.co.uk/ah-dunnichen1856-76.htm
- Angus nonconformist Church Records
  www.personal.dundee.ac.uk/~arnicoll/hist__stuff/church.htm
- St. Andrews, Dundee, Roman Catholic Church registers: Register of Deaths 1804-1816
  www.personal.dundee.ac.uk/~arnicoll/hist__stuff/standrc.htm
- Forfar Old Parish Registers
  www.personal.dundee.ac.uk/~amicoll/hist__stuff/forfarbr.htm
List, with brief extracts
- Monikie Kirkyard Burial Records extracted from the Old Parish Records
  www.monikiescotland.freeserve.co.uk/ah-monburtext.htm

Argyll

- Parochial Registers, Co. of Argyll: Bowmore & Kilarrow
  www.homepages.rootsweb.com/~steve/islay/opr
18-19th c., also includes Kildalton baptisms, marriages, and burials
- Fiche & Film Numbers from the Church of Latter Day Saints pertaining to the Isle of Islay
  homepages.rootsweb.com/~steve/islay/lds__fiche.htm
- Isle of Mull Family History Pages: Burial Index
  web.ukonline.co.uk/ian.phillips/mull/index.htm
Index to burials on Mull, and to Mull burials overseas
- Skipness Parish Marriages, Argyllshire, Scotland
  people.ne.mediaone.net/priestner/Skipness/skipness__marr.txt
1800-21

Ayrshire

- Ayrshire Roots: Burials
  www.ayrshireroots.com/Genealogy/Records/Burial/Burial.htm

- Ayrshire Roots: Civil Registration
  www.ayrshireroots.com/Genealogy/Records/Post%201855/Post%201855.htm
Includes transcripts of some records
- Ayrshire Roots: Old Parish Registers
  www.ayrshireroots.com/Genealogy/Records/OPR/OPR.htm
Includes list
- Stair Parish Church Baptismal Register 1862-1917
  www.stairchurch.homestead.com/Baptismal.html

Buteshire

- Buteshire Family History Project: Old Parochial Register
  www.geocities.com/buteshire/OPRs/opr.htm
For Rothesay; various dates 17-19th c.

Clackmannanshire

- LDS Film Records for the Clackmannanshire Parishes
  www.dgnscrn.demon.co.uk/genuki/CLK/msc/LDSfilms.html
List of old parish register extracts, census returns, and birth, marriage and death records in Latter Day Saints Family History Centres

Dumfriesshire

- Irregular Border and Scottish Runaway Marriages
  www.gro-scotland.gov.uk/grosweb/grosweb.nsf/pages/sumrmar

Fife

- The Old Parish Registers of Fife
  www.ffhsoc.freeserve.co.uk/opr.htm
- Births in Fife
  www.rootsweb.com/~sctfif/ffbrths1.html
Contributors entries, with their email addresses
- Brides in Fife
  www.rootsweb.com/~sctfif/ffmrsb1.html
Contributors entries, with their email addresses

- Deaths & Burials in Fife
  www.rootsweb.com/~sctfif/ffdths1.html
Contributors items, with their email addresses

- Grooms in Fife
  www.rootsweb.com/~sctfif/ffmrsg1.html

- Anstruther-Easter Burials (1836-1854) from the Lair Register
  www.ffhsoc.freeserve.co.uk/aneastburials.htm

- Anstruther Free Church Births and Baptisms 1843-47
  www.ffhsoc.freeserve.co.uk/anstfreech.htm

- Auchtermuchty Free Church, later U.F.Martyrs Births Baptisms & Marriages 1843-1854
  www.ffhsoc.freeserve.co.uk/amfreech.htm

- Balmerino Deaths 1823-1854
  www.ffhsoc.freeserve.co.uk/balmerino.htm

- Bethelfield Up Church, Kirkcaldy: baptisms 1854-1854
  www.ffhsoc.freeserve.co.uk/bethelfieldup.htm

- Cameron Burials 1842-1854
  www.ffhsoc.freeserve.co.uk/cameron.htm

- Ceres Associate Congregation: baptisms 1738-1806, 1808, 1836-37
  www.ffhsoc.freeserve.co.uk/ceresac.htm

- Associate Congregation, Crail: Baptisms 1821-1852 (with gaps)
  www.ffhsoc.freeserve.co.uk/crailbaptisms.htm

- Creich and Flisk Free Church Baptisms and Marriages 1843-1854
  www.ffhsoc.freeserve.co.uk/creichflisk.htm

- Baptisms: North-Parish-Church, Dunfermline, 1851-1854
  www.ffhsoc.freeserve.co.uk/dunfnthbapt.htm

- Dysart St. Serf's Interments (1795-1899)
  www.ffhsoc.freeserve.co.uk/dysartstserf.htm

- Dysart Relief Church: Baptisms 1828-1831
  www.ffhsoc.freeserve.co.uk/dysartrelch.htm

- Invertiel Baptisms 1844-1854
  www.ffhsoc.freeserve.co.uk/invertiel.htm

- Kennoway Baptisms 1848-1854: United Presbyterian Church
  www.ffhsoc.freeserve.co.uk/kennupch.htm

- Kilconquhar Burials 1847-1854
  www.ffhsoc.freeserve.co.uk/Kilconqburials.htm

- West United Presbyterian Church, Leslie: Baptisms 1849-1854
  www.ffhsoc.freeserve.co.uk/lesliewupch.htm

- Leven Relief Church: Baptisms 1834-1854
  www.ffhsoc.freeserve.co.uk/levenbaptisms.htm

- Logie Burials 1816-1854
  www.ffhsoc.freeserve.co.uk/logie.htm

- Markinch Burials 1799-1854
  www.ffhsoc.freeserve.co.uk/markinchburials.htm

- Monimail Deaths 1848-1854 (from the communion roll)
  www.ffhsoc.freeserve.co.uk/monimail.htm

- Newburgh Associate Congregation: Marriages & Baptisms 1785-1812 & 1821-1849
  www.ffhsoc.freeserve.co.uk/newburghac.htm

- Pathhead Baptisms 1750-1854: Pathhead Associate Congregation
  www.ffhsoc.freeserve.co.uk/pathheadac.htm

- Pittenweem (St. Johns) Episcopal: Baptisms, Marriages & Deaths 1799-1854
  www.ffhsoc.freeserve.co.uk/pweemepiscopal.htm

Kinrossshire

- LDS Film Records for the Kinross Parishes
  www.dgnscrn.demon.co.uk/genuki/KRS/misc/LDSfilms.html
Parish registers, civil registration records, and census returns.

Kirkcudbrightshire

- Deaths from the OPRs
  www.old-kirkcudbright.net/genealogy/deaths.htm
Kirkcudbright, 1826-53

- Buittle Old Parish Records
  www.buittle.freeserve.co.uk/opr__s.htm

Lanarkshire

- OPR extracts for Lanark County
  www.ktb.net/~dwills/scotref/o-621-660.htm
LDS film nos.

- Civil Records for Lanark County 1855-1867
  www.ktb.net/~dwills/scotref/c-621-660a.htm
LDS film nos.

- Civil Records for Lanark County 1868-1891
  www.ktb.net/~dwills/scotref/c-621-660b.htm
LDS film nos.

Orkney

- Orkney Genealogy Website
  www.cursiter.com/
Includes many pages of birth marriage and death records for particular families

- South Ronaldsay and Burray Civil Death Registers: extracted index
  home.earthlink.net/~southronaldsay/

Roxburghshire

- Index to James Wilson's Register of Deaths
  www.genuki.org.uk/big/sct/ROX/Hawick/wilson.html
For Hawick, 1825-62

Shetland

- Births, Deaths and Marriages in Shetland
  www.karratha.com/~bruce.smith/

Stirlingshire

- Stirlingshire Marriage Index 1855
  www.rootsweb.com/~sctsti/1855mar.htm

Census

- Census Online
  www.census.pro.gov.uk
Public Record Office site, including details of the 1901 census release

- Census Leaflets
  www.pro.gov.uk/research/leaflets/censusmain.htm
Separate leaflets for each census 1841-91, from the Public Record Office

- Scotland: Census
  www.genuki.org.uk/big/sct/Census.html

- Scottish Census Records
  www.scotlandsclans.com/census.htm
Gateway site - but not many listed

- Scotland Genealogy: census records
  www.rootsweb.com/~genclass/205/gen205__4.htm
Introductory tutorial

- Census Films
  www.ktb.net/~dwills/scotref/13311-censusfilms.htm
List of microfilm of Scottish censuses

Argyll

- Account of Population in Parish of Kildalton taken in February 1860
  homepages.rootsweb.com/~steve/islay/rawdata/kild1860.htm

- 1841 census: Skipness Village, Skipness Parish, Argyllshire Co., Scotland
  people.ne.mediaone.net/priestner/skipness/C1841__village.htm

Ayrshire

- Ayrshire Roots: Census Returns
  www.ayrshireroots.com/Genealogy/Records/Census/Census.htm

- Ayrshire Data from Census OPRs & Kirk Sessions
  www.rootsweb.com/~sctayr/census.html

- Census of the Town and Parish of Maybole 1861
  www.maybole.org/history/Archives/morsels/
  MayboleCensusSummary1861%20.gif

- Stair 1851 Census
  home.clara.net/iainkerr/genuki/AYR/Stair/1851census.htm

Buteshire

- Buteshire Family History Project: Census transcription
  www.geocities.com/buteshire/Census/census.htm
  1861 transcripts for Cumbray, Kilbride, Kilmorey, and Rothesay

Dumfriesshire

- Dumfriesshire Census 1851
  homepages.rootsweb.com/%7Escottish/DumfriesCensus1851.html
  Extracts only

East Lothian

- Scottish Census, Haddingtonshire Haddington 1851 2% census
  www.david.thewalkers.com/page38.htm

Fife

- Fife 1851 census strays found in England
  www.fifepost.freeserve.co.uk/censusstraysinengland.htm

Invernessshire

- Terry's Relative Finder
  www.relys4u.f2s.com/
  1841 census for Barra, Bracadale and Durinish, Skye

Kirkcudbrightshire

- Buittle Census Returns 1841, 1851, 1861 & 1881
  www.buittle.freeserve.co.uk/

Lanarkshire

- Indexes to 1851 census of Lanarkshire outwith Glasgow
  www.desgarrity.pwp.blueyonder.co.uk/1851census.htm
  Details of fiche index

- Indexes to the 1861 census returns of the Registration Districts of Lanarkshire
  www.desgarrity.pwp.blueyonder.co.uk/1861census.htm
  Details of a project in progress

Midlothian

- Scottish Census, Duddingston, Edinburgh 1851 2% census
  www.geocities.com/Athens/Aegean/9315/page37.htm

- Scottish Census, Midlothian, Lasswade 1851 2% census
  www.david.thewalker.com/page105.htm

Moray

- Bellie Census 1851
  www.duffus.com/bellie__census1851.htm

Orkney

- Egilsay 1891 census
  www.genuki.org.uk/big/sct/OKI/Rousay/egilsay1891.html

- Papa Westray Census 1841
  www.btinternet.com/~alan.price/papay/pwcensus1841.htm
  Ditto for 1851, /pwcensus1851.htm

- Rousay 1891 census
  www.genuki.org.uk/big/sct/OKI/Rousay/rousay1891a.html
  Continued in /rousay1891b.html and /rousay1891c.html

- Wyre 1891 census
  www.genuki.org.uk/big/sct/OKI/Rousay/wyre1891.html

Perthshire

- Dull 1851
  www.geocities.com/jccglass/dullcensus/1851.html
  Census

- Parish of Dunning: Census of 1871
  www.dunning.mcmail.com/census.html

Ross & Cromarty
- Altandhu
  freepages.genealogy.rootsweb.com/≈coigach/altandhu.htm
Census transcripts 1841-91

- Notes for Reiff, Camusglassellan, & Faochag
  freepages.genealogy.rootsweb.com/~coigach/reiff.htm
Census transcripts for Reiff, 1841-91

Roxburghshire
- 1851 Census transcription, Castleton, Roxburghshire
  www.maxwells.freeserve.co.uk/index.htm

Church Records
- Scotland: Church Records
  www.genuki.org.uk/big/sct/ChurchRecords.html

- Protestant Nonconformity in Scotland: an introduction
  www.genuki.org.uk/big/sct/noncon1.html
Continued at **/noncon2.html**

Angus
- Glamis Heads of Families, 1834
  www.personal.dundee.ac.uk/~arnicoll/hist__stuff/glamis1834.htm
In communion with the Church of Scotland

- Kirkoswald Kirk Session Records
  www.maybole.org/community/kirkoswald/
  kirkoswaldkirksessionrecords.htm

Fife
- Synod and Presbytery Records: Fife
  www.genuki.org.uk/big/sct/FIF/Synod.htm
Locations

Customs and Excise
- Customs and Excise Records: N.A.S. Factsheet
  www.nas.gov.uk/mainframe/fact__sheet/customs.pdf

Directories
Angus
- Dundee Directory 1782
  www.personal.dundee.ac.uk/%7Earnicoll/hist__stuff/dundeedirectory/
  index.htm

- Dundee directory: abstracts from 1782 and 1824
  www.personal.dundee.ac.uk/~amicoll/hist__stuff/abstracts.htm

Ayrshire
- Ayrshire Roots: Directories
  www.ayrshireroots.com/Genealogy/Records/Directories/Directories.htm
List of directories available

- Ayrshire Directories by Pigot & Co 1837
  www.ayrshireroots.com/Genealogy/Reference/1837%20Ayrshire/
  Ayrshire%20Directories.htm

- 1837 Ayrshire Directory by Pigot & Co
  www.maybole.org/history/Archives/1837Directory/index.htm

Berwickshire
- Berwickshire Directories
  www.genuki.org.uk/big/sct/BEW/directories.html
Brief bibliography

See also Roxburghshire

Buteshire
- Buteshire Family History Project: Directories
  www.geocities.com/buteshire/directories/directories.htm
Extracts from *Pigots 1837 directory* relating to the Isle of Arran, Milnport, Rothesay *etc.*

Dumfriesshire
- Directories of Dumfries and Galloway: general directories of Scotland
  www.dgfhs.org.uk/Ian-Anderson/index.htm

Kirkcudbrightshire

- Kirkcudbright Postal Guide, 1921
  www.old-kirkcudbright.net/genealogy/postal-g.htm

Lanarkshire

- First Glasgow Directory 1787
  www.scotlandgenweb.org/archives/glasgowintro.html
Continued by /glasgow.html

- First Glasgow Directory 1787
  www.ayrshireroots.com/Genealogy/Historical/Jones%20Directory.htm

Midlothian

- Edinburgh & Leith County Directories: Corstorphine
  www.angelfire.com/ct2/corstorphine/CorstorphineDirectories.htm
For various years 1842-1905

- Slaters Commercial Directory & topography of Scotland 1852:
Corstorphine, Gogar & Neighbourhood
  www.angelfire.com/ct2/corstorphine/Slaters.html

- 1938-1939. Edinburgh Suburban Directory: Corstorphine
  www.angelfire.com/ct2/corstorphine/1939B.html
Continued in /1939d.html
    /1939i.html
    /1939L.html
    /1939P.html
    /1939S.html and
    /1939Y.html

Peeblesshire

- Peeblesshire Directories
  www.genuki.org.uk/big/sct/PEE/directories.html
Brief list

Roxburghshire

- Roxburghshire directories
  www.genuki.org.uk/big/sct/ROX/directories.html
Brief list

- Rutherfurd's Southern Counties Register and Directory
  www.genuki.org.uk/big/sct/misc/ruth.html
Brief description of an 1866 directory of Roxburghshire, Berwickshire and
Selkirkshire, with notes on facsimile editions

Selkirkshire

- Selkirkshire Directories
  www.genuki.org.uk/big/sct/SEL/directories.html
Brief list

See also Roxburghshire

Wigtownshire

- The Wigtown Directory 1912
  homepages.rootsweb.com/~scottish/tradeDirectory1912.html

Educational Records

- Education: N.A.S. Factsheet
  www.nas.gov.uk/miniframe/fact__sheet/education.pdf

Estate Records

- Estate Records: N.A.S. Factsheet
  www.nas.gov.uk/miniframe/fact__sheet/estaterecords.pdf

- Buildings: N.A.S. Factsheet
  www.nas.gov.uk/miniframe/fact__sheet/buildings.pdf
Sources for house history

- Deeds: N.A.S. Factsheet
  www.nas.gov.uk/miniframe/fact__sheet/deeds.pdf

- Inheriting Land and Buildings: N.A.S. Fact Sheet
  www.nas.gov.uk/miniframe/fact__sheet/inheriting.pdf

- The Register of Sasines: N.A.S. Factsheet
  www.nas.gov.uk/miniframe/fact__sheet/sasines.pdf

- Scotland Genealogy: Land Records - deeds, sasines, and services of heirs
  www.rootsweb.com/~genclass/205/gen205__6.htm
Introductory tutorial

Argyll

- Argyll Estate 1779
  www.geocities.com/Heartland/Park/8997/argyllcensus.htm
  Census of the estate's inhabitants

- Bellonchantuy from the Duke of Argyll's 1792 census
  people.ne.mediaone.net/priestner/skipness/bellochantuigh.txt

- Black Book: list of tenants on the estate of Islay 1828
  homepages.rootsweb.com/~steve/islay/rawdata/blackbook/blackbook.htm

- Kilchoman Islay Rentals 1733-1741
  homepages.rootsweb.com/~steve/islay/rawdata/rentals.htm

Ayrshire

- Ayrshire Roots: Estate and Family Records
  www.ayrshireroots.com/Genealogy/Records/Estate%20and %20Family/Estate%20and%20Family.htm

East Lothian

- Land and Property Records in East Lothian
  freespace.virgin.net/david.howie/genuki/ELN/LandAndProperty.html

Kirkcudbrightshire

- History of the Lands and their Owners in Galloway, by P.H.M'Kerlie, Edinburgh, 1877. Parish of Buittle
  www.buittle.freeserve.co.uk/mckerlie.htm
  Much information on landowners and descent

Land Registry

- Registers of Scotland Executive Agency
  www.ros.gov.uk
  Land Registry; includes information on the Sasines register, service of heirs *etc.*

Monumental Inscriptions

- Scottish Cemetery Records
  www.scotlandsclans.com/cemeteries.htm
  Many pages

- Find a Grave: Scotland
  www.findagrave.com/country/50.html

- Musings from the Cemetery
  www.tartans.com/articles/musingsmain.html
  How to study gravestones

- Saving Graves Scotland
  www.savinggraves.com/scotland/index.htm
  Gateway site

- Jewish Cemeteries in Scotland
  www.jgsgb.ort.org/bury03.htm
  List

Angus

- Selected Cemetery Inscriptions from Balgay Cemetery of Dundee, Scotland
  www.geocities.com/Yosemite/Rapids/6953/balgay.html

- Tombs of the Dundee Howff
  www.geocities.com/dundee__howff/

- Memorial Inscriptions and Photographs of the Older Gravestones situated in the Kirkyard of Monikie parish Kirk, Angus
  www.monikiescotland.freeserve.co.uk/kirkyard.htm

- Memorials at the Graves in Monikie Kirkyard, in Angus, Scotland
  www.monikiescotland.freeserve.co.uk/monkirkgraves.htm

Argyll

- Isle of Islay Cemetery Database
  homepages.rootsweb.com/~steve/islay/cemetery/index.htm

- Skipness Monumental Inscriptions from Kilbrannan Chapel (also known as St. Brendan's and Skipness Chapel)
  people.ne.mediaone.net/priestner/Skipness/mi.htm
  Continued in **/mi2.htm**

- West end (Kilcolmkeil churchyard), Southend parish, Kintyre Peninsula, Scotland
  www.execpc.com/~haroldr/cemetery.htm

Ayrshire
- Ayrshire Roots: Monumental Inscriptions
  www.ayrshireroots.com/Genealogy/Records/Mls/Mls.htm

- Graves and burial records of North Ayrshire and Arran
  www.ayrshireroots.com/Genealogy/Records/Burial/
                                      Burial%20Grounds%20in%20Ayrshire.htm

- Ardrossan Cemetery
  www.headstones.freeserve.co.uk/ardcem.htm

- Monumental Inscriptions for Carrick, Ayrshire
  www.maybole.org/history/books/monumentinscriptions/carrick.htm

- Dalry
  www.headstones.freeserve.co.uk/Dalrycem.htm

- Dreghorn Churchyard Cemetery
  www.headstones.freeserve.co.uk/Dreghorn.htm

- Some Fenwick Churchyard Monumental Inscriptions
  www.ayrshireroots.com/Towns/Fenwick/Fenwick%20Mls.htm

- Irvine Old Kirk Cemetery
  www.headstones.freeserve.co.uk/irvcemo.htm

- Kilbirnie Auld Kirk
  www.headstones.freeserve.co.uk/kilbirni.htm

- Kilmarnock Laigh Kirk
  www.headstones.freeserve.co.uk/KilmLaih.htm

- Kilwinning Abbey Cemetery
  www.headstones.freeserve.co.uk/kilabcem.htm

- Kilwinning Bridgend Cemetery
  www.headstones.freeserve.co.uk/kilbecem.htm

- Knadgerhill Cemetery
  www.headstones.freeserve.co.uk/knadger.htm

- Monumental Inscriptions: Kirkwynd Cemetery, Maybole
  www.maybole.org/history/Archives/kirkwynd/kirkwynd.htm

- Perceton
  www.headstones.freeserve.co.uk/Perceton.htm

- Saltcoats, North Ayrshire Museum Cemetery
  www.headstones.freeserve.co.uk/Saltcoat.htm

- Shewalton Cemetery
  www.headstones.freeserve.co.uk/Shewaltn.htm

- Cemetery Headstone Index: Stair
  www.stairchurch.homestead.com/Headstones.html
  See also **/iNSCRIPTIONS.html**
  and **Inscriptions11.html**

- Stevenston High Kirk Cemetery
  www.headstones.freeserve.co.uk/stevhk.htm

- Stevenston New Street Cemetery
  www.headstones.freeserve.co.uk/stevns.htm

- Stevenston Monumental Inscriptions
  www.ayrshireroots.com/Towns/Stevenston/Stevenston%20Mls.htm

Banffshire
- Annals of Banff Index to the Old Cemetery
  www.geocities.com/kubee21/banff

Buteshire
- Buteshire Family History Project: Cemeteries
  www.geocities.com/buteshire/cemeteries/cemeteries.htm
  Notes from the cemeteries at Kingarth, Rothesay and St. Colmac's

Caithness

- Caithness Cemeteries pre-1855 Tombstone Inscriptions
  homepages.rootsweb.com/~mwi/caithness.txt

Dumfries

- Churches and Graveyards in Dumfries and Galloway
  homepages.rootsweb.com/~dfsgal/index.htm
Photographs only

- Some Gravestones Inscriptions from Dumfries-Galloway
  homepages.rootsweb.com/~scottish/D-Glnscriptions.html

- Annan Tombstone Inscriptions
  www.hawk.37.demon.co.uk/cemeteries/annan-n__cem.html

Dunbartonshire

- Scottish Genealogy Indices
  webite.lineone.net/~gary.young/indice/index.htm
Monumental inscriptions for 12 parishes in Dunbartonshire

- Old Graveyard, Roseneath, Dunbartonshire
  members.madasafish.com/~fairenough/
Monumental Inscriptions

East Lothian

- Memorial Inscriptions
  www.lbes.demon.co.uk/page__5.htm
At Bolton and Saltoun

- St. Mary's Parish Church, Haddington, East Lothian, Scotland: The Graveyard Index
  www.kylemore.btinternet.co.uk/grave.htm
Monumental Inscriptions

- Prestonkirk Burial Ground Survey
  www.ejclark.fsnet.co.uk/survey/index.htm
Includes index to a published transcript

- Memorial Inscriptions Index: Saltoun Churchyard
  www.lbes.demon.co.uk/page__55.htm

Fife

- Cemeteries and Churchyard Records in Fife: where can I find them?
  www.fifepost.freeserve.co.uk/cemeteries.htm

- The Restoration of Tulliallan Kirkyard
  www.rocinante.demon.co.uk/klhg/tullkirk/tullindx.htm

Invernessshire

- Glenurquhart & Glenmoriston Cemetery Inscriptions
  www3.ns.sympatico.ca/bryanfkeddy/Glen9.html

- Tomnahurich Cemetery, Inverness, Scotland
  www.pharmcat.demon.co.uk/cemetery/thurich/index.htm

- Chapel Yard Cemetery, Inverness, Scotland
  www.pharmcat.demon.co.uk/cemetery/chapel/

Kirkcudbrightshire

- Stewartry Kirkyards Illustrated
  www.kirkyards.htm
Notes on a CD concerning gravestones of the Stewartry (or County) of Kirkcudbrightshire

Lanarkshire

- Burial Grounds of Glasgow
  www.headstones.fsnet.co.uk/
Photographs

- Cemeteries and Crematoria in Glasgow
  www.genuki.org.uk/big/sct/LKS/cemeteries-gla.htm
List

- Southern Necropolis Research
  www.southernnec.20m.cem
Glasgow cemetery

- Cemeteries and Crematoria in North Lanarkshire
  www.genuki.org.uk/big/sct/LKS/cemeteries-nl.htm
List

- Cemeteries and Crematoria in South Lanarkshire
  www.genuki.org.uk/big/sct/LKS/cemeteries-sl.htm
List

- Strathaven Cemetery M.I's
  freepages.genealogy.rootsweb.com/~barrie

Midlothian
- Burial Grounds of Edinburgh
  www.headstones.fsnet.co.uk/
Photographs, with some inscriptions, from various cemeteries

Orkney
- Brinian Kirkyard
  www.genuki.org.uk/big/sct/OKI/Rousay/brinian.html

- Egilsay Kirkyard
  www.genuki.org.uk/big/sct/OKI/Rousay/egilsay.htm

- Glebe Kirkyard
  www.genuki.org.uk/big/sct/OKI/Rousay/glebe.html

- Scockness Kirkyard
  www.genuki.org.uk/big/sct/OKI/Rousay/scocknes.html

- Wasbister Kirkyard
  www.genuki.org.uk/big/sct.OKI/Rousay/wasbistr.htm

- Westside Kirkyard
  www.genuki.org.uk/big/sct/OKI/Rousay/westside.html

- Wyre Kirkyard
  www.genuki.org.uk/big/sct/OKI/Rousay/wyre.html

Perthshire
- Cemeteries
  www.taybank.freeserve.co.uk/genuki/PER/cemeteries.html
Lists cemetery records held by Perth & Kinross Council

- Dunning St. Serf's Church Grave Yard Survey
  www.dunning.mcmail.com/gstart.htm

Renfrewshire
- Gravestones
  www.greenockoldwestkirk.freeserve.co.uk/page7.htm
At the Old West Kirk, Greenock

Roxburghshire
- Abbotrule Churchyard: list of surnames
  www.genuki.org.uk/big/set/ROX/Abbotrule/gravelist.html

- Ashkirk Churchyard: list of surnames
  www.genuki.org.uk/big/sct/ROX/Ashkirk/gravelist.html

- Borthwick Wa's Churchyard: list of surnames
  www.genuki.org.uk/big/sct/ROX/Roberton/gravelistB.html

- Cavers Old Churchyard list of surnames
  www.genuki.org.uk/big/sct/ROX/Cavers/gravelist.html

- Roberton Parish Burial Ground: list of surnames
  www.genuki.org.uk/big/sct/ROX/Roberton/gravelistR.html

- Gala Aisle Cemetery
  www.rootsweb.com/~sctsel/Aisle/Aisle.htm

Stirlingshire
- Memorial Inscriptions from Kilsyth Old Churchyard Stirlingshire, Scotland
  members.tripod.com/~Caryl__Williams/Kilsyth-7.html

Municipal and Parochial Records
- Valuation Rolls. N.A.S. Factsheet
  www.nas.gov.uk/miniframe/fact__sheet/valuationrolls.pdf

Angus
- Monikie, Scotland: Valuation Roll 1904-05
  www.monikiescotland/freeserve.co.uk/ah-monikievalroll.htm

Ayrshire

- Ayrshire Roots: Valuation Rolls
  www.ayrshireroots.com/Records/Valuation%20Rolls/
  Valuation%20Rolls.htm

- Maybole Archives Catalog
  www.maybole.org/history/Archives/MayboleArchivesCatalog.htm

- List of Burgesses 15th October 1834
  www.maybole.org/history/archives/morsels/
  ListsofBurgesses15thOctober1834.htm

- Maybole Councillors, 1722-1828
  www.maybole.org/history/Archives/morsels/
  Maybole__Councillors 1722-1828.htm

- The Stent Rolls of Maybole 1816-1832
  www.maybole.org/history/Archives/morsels/
  Maybole__Stent__Rolls__1816-1832.htm

Kirkcudbrightshire

- Ancient Valuation Roll: Parishes of Kirkcudbright, Galtway and Dunrod
  www.old-kirkcudbright.net/owners/ancient.htm

- Kirkcudbright Stent Rolls
  www.old-kirkcudbright.net/genealogy/stent.htm
  For 1779, 1790 and 1806

- Valuation Rolls, Buittle Parish
  www.buittle.freeserve.co.uk/valuation.htm
  Transcripts of 8 rolls, 18-20th c.

Lanarkshire

- A genealogical index to *Extracts from the records of the Burgh of Glasgow,* volume 1 (Minutes & accounts, 1573-1642)
  www.ifb.co.uk/~kinman/gene-index.html

Newspapers

- Online Newspapers.com: Scotland
  www.onlinenewspapers.com/scotland.htm
  Links to Scottish newspaper sites

Angus

- Angus Newspapers
  www.personaldundee.ac.uk/~amicoll/hist__stuff/news.htm
  List

Ayrshire

- Ayrshire Roots: Newspapers
  www.ayrshireroots.com/Genealogy/Records/Newspapers/
  Newspapers.htm
  List

Berwickshire

- Berwickshire newspapers
  www.genuki.org.uk/big/sct/BEW/newspaperList.html
  List of historical newspapers

Poor Law

- The Poor: N.A.S. Factsheet
  www.nas.gov.uk/miniframe/fact__sheet/poor.pdf

Ayrshire

- Ayrshire Roots: Poor Relief Records
  www.ayrshireroots.com/Genealogy/Records/Poor%20Relief/
  Poor%20Relief.htm
  Includes transcripts from Kilwinning and Stevenston, with list of records at Ayrshire Archives, *etc.*

- Dreghorn Poor Relief
  www.troonayrshirefhs.org.uk
  Transcript of the register of applications 1872-90

- Poor Lists
  www.maybole.org/history/Archives/morsels/ListsofPoor.htm
For Maybole

Fife

- Saline Paupers 1845-1852
  www.ffhsoc.freeserve.co.uk/salinepaupers.htm

Kirkcudbrightshire

- Kirkcudbright Parochial Board Appeals, 1848
  www.old-kirkcudbright.net/genealogy.appeals.htm
Appeals against Poor Rate valuations

Registrars

- Registrars Directory
  www.gro__scotland.gov.uk/grosweb/grosweb.nsf/pages/files/$file/
  reglist.pdf

Addresses of Scottish registrars

Angus

- Dundee Registrar of Births, Marriages and Deaths
  www.dundeecity.gov.uk/registrars/main.htm

Ayrshire

- Registration Offices in Ayrshire
  www.rootsweb.com/~sctayr/regaddre.html
Addresses

- Registrars of Births, Deaths and Marriages in Ayrshire
  www.ayrshireroots.com/Genealogy/Records/Registrars/Registrars.htm

Fife

- Registration Offices: Fife
  www.genuki.org.uk/big/sct/FIF/Registrars.htm

Sheriffs Court Records

Angus

- Index to Records of Dundee Sheriff Court
  www.dundee.ac.uk/archives/genuki/ANS/Topics/sc45.html

- Index to Records of Forfar Sheriff Court
  www.dundee.ac.uk/archives/genuki/ANS/Topics/sc47.html

Fife

- Cupar Sheriff Court Aliment Decrees 1830-1854
  www.ffhsoc.freeserve.co.uk/cupardecrees.htm

- Aliment Decrees, Dunfermline Sheriff Court, 1830-1854
  www.ffhsoc.freeserve.co.uk/dunfaliments.htm

- Aberdour Jurors 1851
  www.ffhsoc.freeserve.co.uk/aberdourjurors.htm

- Auchtertool Jurors 1851
  www.ffhsoc.freeserve.co.uk/auchtertooljurors.htm

- Ballingry Jurors 1851
  www.ffhsoc.freeserve.co.uk/ballingryjurors.htm

- Carnock Jurors 1851
  www.ffhsoc.freeserve.co.uk/carnockjurors.htm

- Dalgety Jurors 1851
  www.ffhsoc.freeserve.co.uk/dalgetyjurors.htm

- Saline Jurors 1851
  www.ffhsoc.freeserve.co.uk/salinejurors.htm

- Torryburn Jurors 1851
  www.ffhsoc.freeserve.co.uk/torryburnjurors.htm

Statistical Accounts

- The Statistical Accounts of Scotland 1791-1799 and 1845
  edina.ac.uk/cgi/Statacc.cgi

Tax Records

- Taxation: N.A.S. Factsheet
  www.nas.gov.uk/miniframe/fact__sheet/taxation.pdf

Angus

- Taxation Records
  www.dundee.ac.uk/archives/genuki/ANST/Topics/tax.html
For Angus (Forfarshire)

- Angus Taxations Records
  www.personal.dundee.ac.uk/~amicoll.hist__stuff/tax.htm

Ayrshire

- The Hearth Tax for Ayrshire, 1691
  www.maybole.org/history/Archives/hearthtax1691.htm

Kirkcudbrightshire

- Buittle Horse Tax 1797
  www.kirksyde.freeserve.co.uk/horsetax.htm

- Kirkgunzeon Horse Tax List, 1797
  www.burgoyne.com/pages/djaggi/horsetax/Kirkgunzeon-1798.html

Voluntary Contributors

- Dumfries Weekly Journal 1798: Contribution Lists
  www.old-kirkcudbrightonet/genealogy/17998.htm
List of voluntary contributors to cost of the war

War Memorials, Rolls of Honour *etc.*

- Commonwealth War Graves Commission
  www.cwgc.org/

- Scottish National War Memorial
  www.snwm.org/
Official site

- The Scottish National War Memorial
  www-saw.arts.ed.ac.uk/memorials/SNWM.html
Genuki site

Aberdeenshire

- Corgarff and Strathdon War Memorials
  users.tinyonline.co.uk/amchardy/WarMemorials/Corgarff.htm

- Lumsden War Memorial
  users.tinyonline.co.uk/amchardy/Lumsden/Lumsden.htm

- Towie War Memorial
  users.tinyonline.co.uk/amchardy/Towie/Towie.htm

Angus

- County of Angus Roll of Honour 1914-1919
  vzone.virgin.net/ian.edwards2/index.htm

- Forfar Academy Roll of Honour: the Great War, 1914-1918
  www.personal.dundee.ac.uk/~amicoll/hist__stuff/farh.htm

Ayrshire

- Ayr Cemetery War Graves
  www.scotlandclans.com/ayrmilitary.htm
Burials of servicemen from overseas

- Memorials
  www.maybole.org/history/Archives/Memorials/memorials.htm
War memorials of Maybole

Caithness

- Caithness Roll of Honour 1914-1919 (Army)
  www.internet-promotions.co.uk/archives/caithness/roll/index.htm

Dunbartonshire

- Kirkintilloch War Memorial
  www.geocities.com/Sotto/7309/

- World War I deaths, Kirkintilloch
  ftp.rootsweb.com/pub/wggenweb/scotland/military/www1-a.txt
  Continued by 9 further pages, **ww1-b.txt** *etc.*

Lanarkshire
- List of Fatal Casualties, 1939-45, in Glasgow
  thor.prohosting.com/~hughw/wardead1.txt
  Continued in **wardead2.txt** *etc.*

Midlothian
- Corstorphine War Dead Great War Memorial 1914-1918
  www.angelfire.com/ct2/corstorphine/index8.html
- Corstorphine War Dead 1939-1945
  www.angelfire.com/ct2/corstorphine/index8a.html

Selkirkshire
- Innerleithen War Memorial 1914-1918
  www.rootsweb.com/~sctsel/Innerleith__Memorial.htm

Wills

- Scottish Wills
  www.scan.org.uk/aboutus/WillsMicrosite/willsindex.htm
- Wills and Testaments: N.A.S. Factsheets
  www.nas.gov.uk/miniframe/fact__sheet/wills.pdf
- Scotland Genealogy: probate records and the court system
  www.rootsweb.com/~genclass/205/gen205__7.htm
  Introductory tutorial

Ayrshire
- Ayrshire Roots: testaments, wills, and other source documents
  www.ayrshireroots.com/Genealogy/Records/Wills/WILLs.htm
  Of general Scottish interest, as well as Ayrshire

10. Occupational Records

- Crafts and Trades: N.A.S. Factsheet
  www.nas.gov.uk/miniframe/fact__sheet/crafts.pdf

Airmen
- Royal Air Force and earlier air services: First World War 1914-1918:
  Service Records
  catalogue:pro.gov.uk/External Request.asp?RequestReference=n2049
- Royal Air Force: Second World War 1939-1945: Service Records
  catalogue.pro.gov.uk/ExternalRequest.asp?RequestReference=n2050

Artists
- Glasgow School of Art Archives
  www.gsa.ac.uk/library/archives/index.html

Bankers and Bank Customers
- Royal Bank of Scotland Research Room: Archive Guide
  www.rbs.co.uk/about__us/memorybank/research__room/study/
  default.htm

Book Trades
- Scottish Book Trade Index
  www.nls.uk/catalogues/resources/sbti/
  Index of printers, publishers, bookbinders, etc to 1850

Brewers
- Scottish Brewing Archive
  www.archives.gla.ac.uk/sba/default.html

Clockmakers
- Angus Clockmakers
  www.personal.dundee.ac.uk/~amicoll/hist__stuff/clock.htm

Criminals

- Crime and Criminals: N.A.S. Factsheet
  www.nas.gov.uk/miniframe/fact_sheet/crime.pdf

Footballers

- Scottish Footballers in the Great War
  www.geocities.com/athens/pantheon/3828/

Graduates

- Graduates of Aberdeen University born in Angus
  www.personal.dundee.ac.uk/~amicoll/hist_stuff/abdngrad.htm

Lighthousemen

- Lighthouses: N.A.S. Factsheet
  www.nas.gov.uk/miniframes/fact_sheet/lighthouse.pdf

Medical Professions and Patients

- Royal College of Physicians and Surgeons of Glasgow Library and Archives
  www.rcpsglasg.ac.uk/library.html

- Royal College of Surgeons of Edinburgh Archives
  www.rcsed.ac.uk/geninfo/archive/default.asp

- Greater Glasgow Health Board Archive
  www.archives.gla.ac.uk/gghb/default.html

- Lothian Health Services Archives
  www.lhsa.lib.ed.ac.uk/

For patient and staff records, etc.

Miners

- Scottish Mining
  www.mcpitz.com/

- Bevin Boys
  www-saw.arts.ed.ac.uk/misc/bevin/index.html

Page on young miners 1939-45

- A Database of Mining Deaths in Great Britain
  www.cmhrc.pwp.blueyonder.co.uk/deaths.htm

- Working Bibliography of the History of Coal and Coal Mining in Scotland
  www.ex.ac.uk/~RBurt/MinHistNet/Scotbib.html

- (Part of) Lanark's Mining Industry in 1896: a list of coal mines
  www.tidza.demon.co.uk/1896-08.htm

Completed by:
  www.tidza.demon.co.uk/1896-1922.htm

- Linlithgow's Mining Industry in 1896: a list of coal mines
  www.ex.ac.uk/~RBurt/MinHistNet/1896-09.htm

Names managers

- Edinburgh's Mining Industry in 1896: a list of coal mines
  www.ex.ac.uk/~RBurt/MinHistNet/1896-04.htm

Lists managers

Nurses

- Royal College of Nursing (Scotland): Archives and Oral History Collection
  www.rcnscotland.org/Archivuk.htm

- Royal Navy: Nurses and Nursing Services
  catalogue.pro.gov.uk/ExternalRequest.asp?RequestReference=n2290

Photographers

- Fife Photographers to 1900
  www.ffhsoc.freeserve.co.uk/fifephotogs.htm

Pilots

- Pilots Returns for Aberdeen 1854-1910
  www.geocities.com/SoHo/Workshop/2299/pilots.html

Royal Marines

- Royal Marines: Officers Service Records
  catalogue.pro.gov.uk/ExternalRequest.asp?RequestReference=n2047

- Royal Marines: Other Ranks Service Records
  catalogue.pro.gov.uk/ExternalRequest.asp?RequestReference=n2045
- Royal Marines: Further Areas of Research
  catalogue.pro.gov.uk/ExternalRequest.asp?RequestReference=n2048

Salvationists

- How can I trace information about my Salvationist ancestors?
  www.salvationarmy.org/webmain.nsf/home/homepage
Search 'Ancestors'

Schoolboys

- Kelso Grammar School Prizewinners of 1853
  www.genuki.org.uk/big/sct/ROX/Kelso/1853schoolprizes.html

Seamen (Merchant)

- Merchant Seamen: Records of the RGSS, A Guide to Leaflets
  catalogue.pro.gov.uk/ExternalRequest.asp?RequestReference=n2279

Seamen (Royal Navy)

- Royal Navy: Officers Service Records
  catalogue.pro.gov.uk/ExternalRequest.asp?RequestReference=n2030
- Royal Navy: Officers Service Records, First World War, and
  Confidential Reports 1893-1943
  catalogue.pro.gov.uk/ExternalRequest.asp?RequestReference=n2300
- Royal Navy: Pay and Pension Records: Commissioned Officers
  catalogue.pro.gov.uk/ExternalRequest.asp?RequestReference=n2292
- Royal Navy: Pension Records: Ratings
  catalogue.pro.gov.uk/ExternalRequest.asp?RequestReference=n2294
- Royal Navy: Pension Records: Warrant Officers
  catalogue.pro.gov.uk/ExternalRequest.asp?RequestReference=n2293
- Royal Navy: Ratings Service Records 1667-1923
  catalogue.pro.gov.uk/ExternalRequest.asp?RequestReference=n2031

- Royal Navy: Ratings Entering Service between 1873 and 1923
  catalogue.pro.gov.uk/ExternalRequest.asp?RequestReference=n2034

Caithness

- Caithness Archives Roll of Honour 1914-1919 (Navy)
  www.internet__promotions.co.uk/archives/caithness/roll/navyroll.htm

Soldiers

- The Army list
  catalogue.pro.gov.uk/ExternalRequest.asp?RequestReference=n2017
- Army: muster rolls and pay lists, c1730-1898
  catalogue.pro.gov.uk/ExternalRequest.asp?RequestReference=n2007
- Army Officers Commissions
  catalogue.pro.gov.uk/ExternalRequest.asp?RequestReference=n2286
- Army Officers Records 1660-1913
  catalogue.pro.gov.uk/ExternalRequest.asp?RequestReference=n2004
- Army: Other Ranks: useful sources if you are getting nowhere
  catalogue.pro.gov.uk/ExternalRequest.asp?RequestReference=n2014
- Army: Soldiers Discharge Papers 1760-1913
  catalogue.pro.gov.uk/ExternalRequest.asp?RequestReference=n2005
- Army: Soldiers Pensions 1702-1913
  catalogue.pro.gov.uk/ExternalRequest.asp?RequestReference=n2006
- British Military Records
  www.genuki.org.uk/big/BritMilRecs.html
- Military Records: N.A.S. Factsheet
  www.nas.gov.uk/miniframe/fact__sheet/military.pdf
- Scotland Genealogy Military Records
  www.rootsweb.com/~genclass/205/gen205__9.htm
- Scots at War
  www-saw.arts.ed.ac.uk

- United Kingdom and Ireland Military Records
  www.genuki.org.uk/big/MilitaryRecords.html
Includes links to many Public Record Office leaflets

- Scottish Military Historical Society
  www.btinternet.com/~james.mckay/dispatch.htm

- The Black Watch Archive
  www.blackwatch.50megs.com/
Includes roll of honour 1939-45, and various other name lists

Angus

- Muster Rolls of Angus, Scotland: South African War 1899-1900
  www.monikiescotland.freeserve.co.uk/ah-musterroll.htm

Argyll

- 98th Argyllshire Highlanders 1794
  www.argylls.co.uk/91rlist.html
List

Ayrshire

- Ayrshire's Military History
  home.clara.net/iainkerr/genuki/AYR/military.htm

- Ayrshire Rifle Volunteers: Maybole Company Muster Roll
  www.maybole.org/history/Archives/rifle/volunteers.htm

Caithness

- Highland Archives: Caithness Roll of Honour 1914-1919
  www.iprom.co.uk/archives/caithness/roll/index.htm

Fife

- Fife Military History Society
  freespace.virgin.net/eduard.klak.index.htm

- Loyal Tay Fencibles
  www.ffhsoc.freeserve.co.uk/loyaltay.htm
Various lists of men 1794-1801

Lanarkshire

- Lanarkshire's Heroes
  www.forvalour.com/frames.htm
Victoria Cross medallists

Teachers

- Corstorphine Schoolmasters 1646-1924
  www.angelfire.com/ct2/corstorphine/index7.html

- Corstorphine Teachers
  www.angelfire.com/ct2/corstorphine/index7a.html
From the 1881 census

Theatrical Workers

- Scottish Theatre Archive
  special.lib.gla.ac.uk/STA/index.html

Textile Workers

- The Turkey Red Trust
  www.geocities.com/turkeyredtrust/
Textile industry in the Vale of Leven, 1715-1960

11. Miscellaneous Sites

Adoptees

- Adoptee Search Post
  www.geocities.com/adoptee_search_post/index

- Adoption Records: N.A.S. Family History Factsheet
  www.nas.gov.uk/miniframe/fact_sheet/adoption.pdf

Border Reivers

- Border Reivers
  www.reivers.com/

Churches

- Church Location Database
  www.genuki.org.uk/big/parloc/

- Outline History: Churches in Scotland
  home.clara.net/iainkerr/genuki/AYR/Kirkhist.htm
Time-line setting out 'pedigree' of the various denonimations

- Scotland: Church History
  www.genuki.org.uk/big/sct/ChurchHistory.html

- Splits and Reunions of the Church of Scotland 1560-1929
  www.btinternet.com/~stnicholas.buccleuch/chart.htm

- Churches in Fife in the year 1893
  www.fifepost.freeserve.co.uk/churches.htm

Clans

- Council of Scottish Clans and Associations
  www.tartans.com/cosca

- Gathering of the Clans
  www.tartans.com/

- The Gathering of the Clans
  www.nessie.co.uk/clan/clanindx.html
Find out if you have a 'clan' connection!

- Genealogy Scotland: Clans; history
  members.tripod.com/~Caryl_Williams/scot.html
Gateway

- Map of the Scottish Clans
  www.its.caltech.edu/~gatti/gabaldon/clanmap.html

- What is the History behind the Scottish Clans?
  www.visitscotland.com/faqs/detail_faq.asp?ID=76

Sutherlandshire

- Clans of Sutherlandshire
  members.aol.com/obrienbarb/Scot/SuthGenWebClan.html
Gateway to clan and family homepages, *etc.*

Covenanters

- The Covenanters
  www.tartans.com/articles/cov1.html

Divorce

- Divorce and Separation: N.A.S. Factsheet
  www.nas.gov.uk/miniframe/fact_sheet/divorce.pdf

Emigration

There are numerous sites devoted to Scottish emigration. For introductory websites, see:

- Emigration: N.A.S. Factsheet
  www.nas.gov.uk/miniframe/fact_sheet/emigration.pdf

- Knowledge Base Home: Emigration
  www.scan.org.uk/knowledgebase/topics/emigration_topic.htm
Brief but useful

- Scotland Genealogy: getting your ancestor across the ocean
  www.rootsweb.com/~genclass/205/gen205_1.htm
Introductory guide to sources for emigration

A number of sites provide extensive gateways to the innumerable passenger list websites (which are far too numerous to list here):

- Immigrant Ships Transcribers Guild: Scottish Ports
  istg.rootsweb.com/departures/scotland.html

Continued by:
  istg.rootsweb.com/departuresv2/scotlandv2.html and
  istg.rootsweb.com/departuresv3/scotlandv3.html

- Harold Ralston's links to ship passenger lists
  www.execpc.com/~haroldr/shiplist.htm

- Ship Search: a surname search of passenger lists on the internet
  www.obitcentral.com/shipsearch/

Other miscellaneous sites include:

- Scots in Nova Scotia
  www.chebucto.ns.ca/Heritage/FSCNS/
                  Scots_NS/About_Clans/Scots_NS.html

- The Scots/Irish Immigration of the 1700's
  www.zekes.com/%7Edspidell/famresearch/ulster.html

General history

- Scottish Prisoners Transported to America in the aftermath of Culloden 1746
  www.geocities.com/ResearchTriangle/Lab/4527/shiplists/scotimmi.html

List

Argyll

- I-Spy: Islay Immigrant Index
  www.geocities.com/tgilhuly

Data concerning emigrants from Islay

Ayrshire

- Ayrshire born - foreign buried
  homepage.rootsweb.com/%7Eayrshire/indexforeign.html

Strays from burial records

Fife

- Fife, Scotland (E)migration Patterns Project
  www.rootsweb.com/~sctfif/ffemgr.html

Contributed entries, with contributors email address

Invernessshire

- Hebridean Scots of the Province of Quebec
  www.geocities.com/~hebridscots/contents.htm

- Selkirk settlers identified from past and present of P.E.I., Skye and Hebridean Pioneers
  www.islandregister.com/selkirk_settlers.htm

Passenger list reconstruction for the *Polly*, 1803; emigration promoted by Lord Selkirk

Perthshire

- Emigration from Perthshire to Canada in the early 19th century
  www.taybank.freeserve.co.uk/resources/emigration.html

Scots Overseas
Australia

- Scots Down Under
  www.britannia.com/celtic/scotland/scot19.html

Essay

- Born in the Border Counties of Scotland
  www.genuki.org.uk/big/sct/misc/strays.html

List of emigrants marrying in Victoria, Australia, 1853-95

Canada

- The Scots in Canada
  britannia.com/celtic/scotland/scot18.html

Article

- Emigration Records from England and Scotland to Prince Edward Island
  www.islandregister.com/fhc/engscot.html

- Ayrshire born: buried in Nanaimo, British Columbia, Canada
  www.ayrshireroots.com/Genealogy/Records/Burial/
  Nanaimo%20deaths.htm

- Orkney men with the Hudson's Bay Company
  www.genuki.org.uk/big/sct/OKI/canada.html

- The Perth County Pioneers
  www.tbaytel.net/bmartin/perth.htm
Emigration to Canada from Perthshire

United States

- The Scots in the USA
  britannia.com/celtic/scotland/scot17.html
Article

- The Scottish Connection in Kansas
  skyways.lib.ks.us/genweb/republic/PatAdams/ScotIndex.html
Includes links to surname pages

Events

- GENEVA: an Online Calendar of GENealogical EVents and Activities
  users.ox.ac.uk/~malcolm/genuki/geneva/

Glossaries

- Archival Terms: N.A.S. Factsheet
  www.nas.gov.uk/miniframe/resources/archivalterms.pdf

- Scotland: Glossary of Archive Terms
  pro.wanadoo.fr/euroleader/wedderburn/glossary.htm

- A Scots Glossary
  home.clara__net/iainkerr/genuki/AYR/glossary.htm

Heraldry
- Heraldry in Scotland
  www. kwtelecom.com/heraldry/scother1.htm

- A note on Scots Heraldry
  www.heraldica.org/topics/britain/scotland.htm

- An annotated bibliography of Scottish Heraldic Materials
  www.heraldica.org/topics/britain/scotbiblio.htm

Highland Clearances

- The Highland Clearances
  www.macgowan.org/higclear.html

- The Highland Clearances
  www.theclearances.org

- The Highland Clearances
  members.aol.com/Jimsutherl/clearances.html

- The Scots and the Clearances: the movement of people between Scotland and Ireland, and onward emigration to North America, Australia and New Zealand
  home.clara.net/iainkerr/kerr/clearances.htm
Article

Jacobites
- The Jacobite Risings 1715 and 1745
  catalogue.pro.gov.uk/ExternalRequest.asp?RequestReference=n2128

Jews
- Snippets: Scotland
  www.jgsgb.ort.org/sncscot.htm
For Jews

Lookups
- Books We Own: Scotland
  www.rootsweb.com/~bwo/scotland.html

- Genealogy Helplist United Kingdom: Scotland
  www.cybercomm.net/~freddie/helplist/uk.htm#Scot

- Scotland
  www.rootsweb.com/~bwo/scotland.html
Lookup site

- Scotland Look-up Exchange
  www.geocities.com/Heartland/Acres/6317/sct.htm

Argyll
- Islay Virtual Library
  homepages.rootsweb.com/~steve/islay/library.htm
Look-ups offered

Ayrshire
- Ayrshire look-ups
  home.clara.net/iainkerr/genuki/AYR/lookups.htm

Dunbartonshire
- Lennox lookups
  www.geocities.com/lennoxlookups/

- Volunteers and Look-ups
  www.rootsweb.com/~sctdub/lookups.html
Lookups offered for Dunbartonshire and Scotland in general

East Lothian
- Look-up Volunteers
  hometown.aol.com/eastlothiangen/volunteers.htm
For East Lothian sources

Fife
- Fife (Scotland) Genealogy Resource Providers
  www.fifepost.freeserve.co.uk/resources.htm

Lanarkshire
- Lookups
  www.rootsweb.com/~sctlks/lookups.htm
For Lanarkshire

Missing People
- Lookup UK.com
  www.lookupuk.com/
Site for finding missing people

- Salvation Army Family Tracing Service
  www.salvationarmy.org.uk/family tracing/index.html

Name Origins
- Scottish Names
  roisindubh.tripod.com/Scottish/index.html
Find names with Scottish roots

- Scottish Names Resources
  www.medievalscotland.org/scotnames/
Collection of articles on Scottish personal names

- Scottish Surnames
  www.david.thewalkers.com/page127.htm
Gives early locations and clans

- Scottish Surnames
  www.cproots.com/surnameorigins/namesystems/namsyssct.htm
Discussion of names and their origins

Aberdeenshire
- Aberdeenshire Personal Names
  www.urie.demon.co.uk/genuki/ABD/names.html
Discussion of naming practices

Palaeography
- Scottish Genealogy. Scottish Handwriting and common terms
  www.rootsweb.com/~genclass/gen205__8.htm

- Scottish Handwriting
  www.scan.org.uk/researchtools/handwriting/scottishhandwriting.htm

Pedigrees

- United Kingdom and Ireland Records
  userdb.rootsweb.com/uki/
Search records for c.250,000 individuals

Aberdeen

- From Aberdeenshire to the Ends of the Earth
  www.j.mann.taylor.clara.net/family.htm
Substantial collection of Aberdeenshire pedigrees

Ayrshire

- Ayrshire Roots: Surname Database
  www.ayrshireroots.com/Genealogy/Database/database.html
See also
  www.ayrshireroots.com/Genealogy/Surnames/index.html
Pedigrees

Royalty

- Scotland Royal Genealogy
  www.scotlandroyalty.org/

- Scotland Royal Genealogy
  www.rootsweb.com/~txhall/scotland.html

- The Scottish Monarchy
  www.highlanderweb.co.uk/monarch1.htm

Strays

- Sutherland, Scotland strays list
  members.aol.com/sloinne/Sutherland/Suth__Strays.htm
Mainly overseas

Tartans

- Tartans of Scotland
  www.tartans.scotland.net

12. Gazetteers and Maps

The family historian will frequently need to identify places mentioned in the sources he uses. There are a number of web-based gazetteers which will enable him to do this:

- Gazetteer for Scotland
  ww.geo.ed.ac.uk/scotgaz

- United Kingdom and Ireland Gazetteers
  www.genuki.org.uk/big/Gazetteers.html

- Place Names Lists
  www.origins.net/GRO/Places/places.html

- Ordnance Survey Landranger Search
  www.ordsvy.gov.uk/products/Landranger/lrmsearch.cfm
For locating places in Scotland, as well as England and Wales

An awareness of the historic administrative divisions of Scotland is also important, since they may determine the location of sources. For these, consult:

- Administrative Areas of Scotland
  www.genuki.org.uk/big/Regions/Scotland.html

For a map of the historic Scottish counties, see:

- Scottish Counties before 1974
  www.rootsweb.com/~sctayr/counties.jpg

There are many map sites on the internet. Amongst the more useful are:

- Genmaps: old maps of Great Britain
  freepages.genealogy.rootsweb.com/~genmaps/index.html
On-line historic maps

- National Library of Scotland Map Library
  www.nls.uk/collections/maps

- **Old Maps.co.uk**
  www.old-maps.co.uk
  On-line Ordnance Survey maps

County Map Sites

Ayrshire

- Outline Parish Maps: Ayrshire
  home.clara.net/iainkerr/genuki/AYR/ayrparish.htm

- Ayrshire Parish Map
  home.clara.net/iainkerr/genuki/AYR/ayr__pmap.htm

- County of Ayrshire
  www.rootsweb.com/~sctayr/ayr.jpg
  Parish map

Berwickshire

- Berwickshire Gazetteer
  www.vivdunstan.clara.net/genuki/BEW/gazetteer/

Dumfriesshire

- Dumfriesshire Parish Map
  www.embra.force9.co.uk/genuki/DFS/Parishes/parish__map.html

Dunbartonshire

- Dunbartonshire Parish Map
  www.skyline.net/~lasmith/genuki/DNB/dnbpmap.html

East Lothian

- Genmap: Old Maps of East Lothian
  genealogy.rootsweb.com/~genmaps/genfiles/
  COU__Pages/SCO__pages/eln.htm

Fife

- Map showing the Parishes of Fife
  www.fifepost.freeserve.co.uk/map.htm

Kincardineshire

- Kincardineshire Parish Map
  www.genuki.org.uk/big/sct/KCD/ParishMap.html

Lanarkshire

- County of Lanark
  www.rootsweb.com/~sctayr/lanark.jpg
  Parish map

Peeblesshire

- Peeblesshire Map
  www.genuki.org.uk/big/sct/PEE/map.html

Roxburghshire

- Roxburghshire Gazetteer
  www.vivdunstan.clara.net/genuki/ROX/gazetteer

- Roxburghshire Maps
  www.genuki.org.uk/big/sct/ROX/mapList.html

Selkirkshire

- Selkirkshire Map
  www.genuki.org.uk/big/sct/SEL/map.html

- Selkirkshire Maps
  www.genuki.org.uk/big/sct/SEL/mapList.html
  List

13. Professional Services, Booksellers etc.

A.   Professional Genealogists

The websites of professional genealogists are not listed here. If you do want to employ a professional to undertake research, you should first visit:

- Association of Scottish Genealogists and Record Agents
  www.asgra.co.uk

See also:

- Genealogy Pro: Professional Genealogists and Genealogy Research Services for Scotland
  www.genealogy.com/directories/Scotland.html
  List of researchers

For professional researchers willing to undertake work at the Public Record Office, consult:

- Independent Researchers
  www.pro.gov.uk/research/rrlist/default.htm

B. Other Services

- Abeshaus
  www.abeshaus.com/new/Genealogy/scottish.htm
  American bookshop

- Appleton's
  www.appletons.com
  Over 100 Scottish genealogical books for sale in the USA

- Archive CD Books: Scottish Counties
  www.rod-neep.co.uk/acatalog/Archive__CD__Books__Scotland__13.html
  CD's

- Audiotapes.com
  www.audiotapes.com/search2.asp?Search=Scotland
  Audiotapes on Scottish genealogy

- The Best Books on Scotland
  www.scotland-inverness.co.uk/scotbks.htm
  Bookseller

- David Dobson, M.Phil.
  www.users.zetnet.co.uk/dobson.genealogy/
  Professional genealogist's page, but included here for the extensive listing of Dobson's books for the Scottish family historian

- Frontier Press Bookstore
  www.frontierpress.com/frontier.cgi?category=scot
  Good list of books on Scottish genealogy

- Genealogical Publishing Co.
  www.genealogical.com/search__locality1.cfm?string=Scotland/Scottish
  Books from Genealogical Publishing Co.

Subject Index

Institution Index

Place Index